FROST AND THE FRUITGROWER

1

Frost-Damaged Pears above and Apples below. A single sound fruit is included for comparison.

FROST AND
THE FRUITGROWER

BY

RAYMOND BUSH

WITH AN INTRODUCTION BY
THE RT. HON. THE EARL OF SELBORNE

WITH 23 HALF-TONE PLATES
AND 15 ILLUSTRATIONS IN THE TEXT

CASSELL
and Company, Ltd.
London, Toronto, Melbourne
and Sydney

First edition September 1945
Second edition February 1946
Third edition November 1947

PRINTED IN GREAT BRITAIN BY
BUTLER AND TANNER LTD., FROME AND LONDON

247

CONTENTS

LIST OF ILLUSTRATIONS

(From photographs by the Author except where otherwise stated)

INTRODUCTION

BY THE EARL OF SELBORNE, P.C.

IT is well that Mr. Bush has written this book. As one of the many fruit-farmers who are indebted to him for wise advice on the numerous problems that beset growers, I know that there is no one better qualified to expound the principles that should be in the mind of every intending grower before planting.

There is nothing more exasperating than to plant an orchard and, after all the capital expenditure has been incurred, to discover that in alternate years it will bear no fruit because it has been planted in a frost pocket.

When I started to grow fruit I knew very little about it, and in this I imagine I was not peculiar, because it is only by trying to grow fruit that we discover our ignorance of the art. I remember havering between two alternative sites. A well-known and successful fruit-grower advised me to plant on one, but I had an idea that I should get a better colour by planting on another about a mile away, and so I did. Nobody advised me that one was frost-free whilst the other was a frost pocket, because I had not yet met Mr. Bush. By sheer good luck I planted in the right place. I have often thought what losses I should have incurred if I had planted on the other site. When Mr. Bush saw my plantations he was able to explain to me why they were unlikely ever to be seriously frosted, whereas the other site was a death trap to fruit blossom.

The author possesses that rare combination—the scientific and the literary mind. He is therefore able to do what many scientists cannot do, i.e. to explain in language understanded of the people the scientific reasons for Nature's vagaries : and in him wisdom is made more welcome by being well wrapped in wit.

I therefore recommend this book to those who are contemplating planting fruit. In post-war England we shall be more dependent on home-grown fruit than in the days when we were rich enough to buy everything we required from abroad. The British public like to have their fruit every year and will not be content to partake of it only in non-frost years. Our home-grown fruit industry cannot expect to flourish unless it can supply its customers regularly. Continuity of supply is the first requisite of successful marketing.

Let us hope, therefore, that fruitgrowers will select frost-free sites in future. This book will help them to do that.

S.

April 5, 1945.

CHAPTER I

THIS FRUITGROWING

WE in England know very little about the statistical side of our industry. At intervals we are supplied with forward estimates of crops which from past experience we know to be premature, extremely unreliable, and liable to correction when the last Spring frost has had its way sometime in May.

Our last published Official Publication—*Fruit*, 1937—for example, tells us that we had, in 1936, a matter of 16,900,000 apple trees growing on 191,000 acres and 1,950,000 pear trees spread over some 17,216 acres. They do not tell us what proportion of those apples and pears were good, bad or indifferent, dessert or cooking, cider or perry. Nor are we informed how many acres are freshly planted, mature or well on the way to decay. Nor have we any idea of the average value of our fruit crops.[1]

[1] Since this chapter was written the Ministry of Agriculture published, in November 1944, the preliminary results of a Fruit Census of England and Wales which included all holdings of more than one acre in extent.

Some extraordinary conditions were brought to light. The total number of trees of dessert apples of all varieties are estimated at 9,022,300. Of these 4,704,200 are Cox's Orange Pippins and 1,533,300 are Worcester Pearmain trees.

The figures describing density of planting show that among trees of Cox of nine years old or over, numbering in all 1,590,800, only 116,700 were planted at under one hundred to the acre or about twenty feet apart. 850,300 were planted at from one to five hundred to the acre or from twenty to nine feet apart, and 623,800 were planted at over five hundred to the acre or about nine feet or less apart. This last figure includes the intensively planted trees of cordon and dwarf pyramid types which may be set out as thickly as 2,420 trees to the acre.

When we turn to trees of under nine years planted which, of course, includes the heavy plantings of just before the War, Cox give 57,300 trees at under a hundred to the acre, and 609,700 at one to five hundred an acre. The figure for plantings at over five hundred to the acre rises sharply to 2,446,400 trees.

These figures are interesting since the planting distance recommended to-day for a bush Cox on a moderately dwarfing stock (E.M. Type 2) is twenty feet apart. Some authorities prefer twenty-four feet apart. If the square method of planting is adopted the former figure gives one hundred and four and the latter seventy-five trees to the acre.

From this it will be realised that the danger of over-crowding trees is a very real one. The sudden rise to over two million of the ultra-close planted trees can be disregarded as this was mainly due to the activities of a single firm operating on an "Own your own apple tree" type of slogan, and since the setting out of two million trees at say one hundred trees to the acre would occupy twenty thousand acres of land, close planting alone could accomodate the number. Crop results of this type of planting are not yet forthcoming, but the planting of a concentration of over two thousand

1

If one enquires of the Canadian Government as to the fruit growing in that country an immense amount of tabulated data is forthcoming. For each province you may have the description, variety, quantity and average price of the trees and plants sold by the various nurserymen of the particular province. The quantity and value of each variety of fruit produced in the previous season can be compared with the preceding season. If you require it you will be supplied with the number of trees of any variety of the various fruits for any district, whether they are of bearing age or not, the amount of fruit produced and the value of that fruit. In fact what the Dominion Bureau of Statistics at Ottawa does not know about the Canadian orchards is not worth knowing.

It may be that our own lack of knowledge is a merciful dispensation of Providence, or a blissful ignorance which it would be foolish to question; for our own fruit production is a most uncertain factor, liable to extreme shortages and embarrassing gluts. In apples alone our production varied from 116,000 tons in 1931 to 527,000 tons in 1934, as compared with Canada's 231,000 tons in 1931, and 330,000 in 1933, both figures giving the minimum and maximum crops between 1931 and 1937. The fact of the matter is that many of our orchards are badly sited and liable to extreme damage from spring frosts.

Comparison of the crop figures from frosty and frost-free fruit districts shows clearly what the cost of a chilly night or two in May can be. If we compare the average annual crop of apples from the United Kingdom with those of Canada, the United States and Australia, their steadiness and our instability are all too obvious.

trees to the acre on any but the ideal site is fraught with grave danger unless the principles of air drainage in relation to the chosen site are clearly understood and carefully applied.

It is gratifying to see that in the figures relating to cooking apples no more than 4,100 trees of Bramley's Seedling have been planted at over five hundred to the acre during the past nine years, while 166,500 were planted at less than a hundred to the acre. Of the trees of this variety over nine years planted 1,082,400 are at less than a hundred trees to the acre, 824,300 are far too close at one to five hundred to the acre and Heaven alone knows what 11,600 trees of this variety were doing at over five hundred to the acre.

With Bramley an immensely strong-growing variety and almost if not quite the most frost susceptible apple we have, those 11,600 trees are likely to be unproductive in any frost year. It becomes clear that the need for the formation of a Society for the Prevention of Cruelty to Young Apple Trees is long overdue.

The Fruit Census figures which include Apples, Pears, Cider and Perry fruit, Plums, Cherries, Nuts and the soft fruits are a good beginning, and from such figures one can draw all kinds of interesting and instructive conclusions.

Production in thousands of tons :

Country	1932	1933	1934	1935	1936	Max. Variation
England and Wales	160	214	527	133	511	298%
Australia . . .	181	212	206	188	..*	17%
Canada	241	330	262	271	247	37·5%
U.S.A.	3017	3064	2586	3584	2518	30%

* The Australian figure for 1936 was not issued in the last Government publication dealing with Fruit Supplies in 1937.

It is a noticeable fact also that, as regards production per tree or per acre, even in their worst season, Canadian cropping is more than double that of trees in the United Kingdom and this variation persists. It is an extremely important point to remember, that while our crop variation may be from 1 to 5, that of the U.S.A. and our Dominions only swings between 1 and 1·75.

For this reason our own fruit marketing is not self-stabilising but is at the mercy of the overseas exporter and the home importer, who see to it that no real shortage of any particular fruit (which might have resulted in high prices for the fortunate home grower with a good crop) can occur. Such stabilisation may be good for the masses, the merchants, the middlemen and the retailers, but it makes hard going for the average fruitgrower in peacetime.

It can only be ignorance of the true state of affairs which impelled Lord Addison in *A Policy for British Agriculture* to suggest that we need 400,000 more acres of fruit- and vegetable-growing. This he claims could be made profitable by better distribution, but if our fruit and vegetables were better distributed have we any guarantee that the mass of foreign fruit and vegetables,[1] many of which are sold at very low prices, would not share in that improved distribution ?

As regards fruit, and some vegetable crops, the fact of the matter is that while American and Dominion growers have learned to assess the liability of land to frost damage in Spring, and to plant out accordingly, a very large proportion of our English fruit can only mature to full weight and perfection if the season happens to be a kindly one. Our climate may be changing, or we may be

[1] In pre-war days Mussolini's draining of the Pontine Marshes was very soon followed by an export to Britain of Italian cauliflowers.

passing through a cycle of frosty Springs, but the fact remains that year after year certain well-chosen sites escape all frost damage, while others less favourably situated lose from 5 to 85 per cent. of their crop in a bad year.

It is not chance which causes these discrepancies in cropping. The reasons for it are known, and there can be little doubt that it is infinitely more important that future plantings should be chosen to replace, so far as may be possible, our existing vulnerable acreage on well-chosen sites, than to talk grandiosely of thousands more acres when fully two-thirds of what we have is only half-productive.

Supposing that we assume that a benevolent Government is anxious to develop fruit-growing in England on a large scale, how, then, can the future of fruit-growing be safeguarded?

We know that thousands of acres of arable land under farm crops are excellently sited for fruit-growing, and thousands of acres of fruit would be far better under arable crops. There is no magician who can wave his magic wand with a " Hey! Presto! Pass! " and exchange the two sites.

If Nationalisation of the Land ever comes to pass, and in these uncertain days no change is too unlikely to imagine, then there should be a site survey and those excellently sited, frost-free arable acres should be ear-marked for future orchards as the tenant dies or gives up the farm.

To-day one can search the Country for an available fruit farm which combines the virtues of good soil and good air drainage. Such are not the orchards which come into the market at the present price of land. As a result the beginner is often forced to buy the wrong land at the wrong price and makes a failure. If he is lucky under war-time conditions he may find another beginner to buy it and so cut his losses and pass on the curse.

We live from hand to mouth. We saw fruit boom in the last war. We saw the slump after and many felt it despite the nest egg which the war years had donated. E.P.T. has seen to it that the present War's nest eggs are few and far between.

It is for such reasons that the author of this book prefers to omit statistics and inspired propaganda relative to possible and impossible development and demands, and confines himself to the purely practical side of frost in relation to fruit-growing with enough simplicity to assist the beginner and enough technicality to interest and perhaps aid the established orchardist.

CHAPTER II

WHAT FROST MEANS TO THE FRUITGROWER

IF we take the cropping figures from a large fruit farm frost-free in some parts but liable to the extreme of damage in others and compare the annual yield with the United Kingdom production figures we get the following. They clearly relate an individual crop to the National output.[1]

Year.	Crop from one farm.	United Kingdom Crop.
1934	75,000 bushels	527,000 tons
*1935	10,000 ,,	133,000 ,,
1936	100,000 ,,	511,000 ,,
1937	15,000 ,,	165,650 ,,
*1938	5,000 ,,	126,150 ,,

Of the five years recorded the two marked * are years of major frost damage. The season of 1934 was one of our heaviest glut crops (exceeded only by that of 1939 which followed a frost year). The result of the 1935 and 1938 frosts was to allow the trees to put away an unusually large reserve of carbohydrates which are needed for fruit bud production. Tremendously heavy blossom and freedom from frost in both following years gave glut crops again in 1936 and 1939.

The result of the glut crop is to debilitate the tree and bring what fruitgrowers describe as an "off-year." This inability to crop after an over-crop is very pronounced in certain varieties, Ellison's Orange, Laxton's Superb, Miller's Seedling and Newton Wonder being recognised types of the biennial bearing tree and somewhat elaborate technique in pruning, thinning and manuring is needed to overcome this habit. Other varieties, given enough manure, can be relied upon to crop regularly, consistently and heavily without showing any pronounced signs of the biennial

---

[1] How unreliable our official figures may be in suggesting our total crop of fruit-grower produced apples can be gauged by the following fact. The official estimate over a period of years of U.K.-grown fruit (edible, and cooking, and cider) allows 25 per cent. of the total for cider fruit. Yet the 1937 crop of cider fruit was approximately half the total fruit of the country. A frost which sweeps the South, South-east, and East is less likely seriously to affect the West, where cider apples are grown; so that in any frosty year cider apples are likely to be far above the official 25 per cent estimate.

5

habit. Frost, however, remains the main originator of alternate year cropping.

The poor crop figure of the year 1937, following the glut crop of 1936, was not caused by frost but was in part the natural reaction to over-heavy cropping. The blossom season, however, in 1937 was an exceptionally unfavourable one with much rain, high air humidity and a minimum of sunshine. Under such conditions pollen does not " run " well, bees are unable to work and the flower instead of being a scented, nectar-filled thing of beauty is just a mess. Blossom is very much at the mercy of the weather and fine sunny weather in May means a heavy set of what blossom is available. The year 1944, for example, provided ideal pollinating weather in April and May and where frost did not strike unduly hard an extremely heavy set of fruit (often carrying the " frost-eye " indicative of a major freeze) developed and matured.[1]

The poor pollination of 1937 should have been followed by another glut year in 1938, but in April and May frost stepped in and down went our production figures once more. Since the figures of crop yields are very largely influenced by the Bramley crop, and since this apple is the most susceptible of any to frost damage, the need for keeping this variety well up out of the frosty levels and flats will be realised; yet one of the great Bramley-producing centres is the low-lying area of the Weald of Kent. It is the failure of such areas to crop regularly which provide the market with its greatest problem—stability and reliability of supplies.

There are very big areas in Kent admirably situated to escape frost damage but so badly laid out, so overgrown and neglected that their crop potential is almost at zero. Since the War began much clearance and thinning out or even complete grubbing of some of these areas has been ordered or even undertaken by the Kent War Agricultural Executive Committee and some surprising results have followed where cultivation and spraying of thinned-out orchards is intelligently and efficiently pursued.

A certain number of growers, realising the value of site, had before the War spent much time and money on opening out these fruit jungles and the one illustrated, facing page 88, is a sample of

[1] As I corrected these proofs in the last week of April, 1945, the apple blossom was already almost over after an incredibly rapid development under ideal conditions for pollination. Frosts had already taken some toll, but with so tremendous a set of fruit even a 50 per cent. thin out would be a blessing. Later corrections on May 12 have been made and it now becomes obvious that the frosts of the first two nights of May have brought the year 1945 into a major frost status.

the condition of many hundreds of acres of valuable orchard land. The illustration, upper half of Plate 20, shows a nice young orchard of Bramleys. It is hard to realise that a few years earlier this orchard was a jungle which could not even be walked through. The original plant was of Bramleys at 30 feet. Plums were interplanted at 15 feet; nuts at 7 feet 6 inches, with red currants set between them; and strawberries as a final touch. Once such a plant has been allowed to go wild and brambles have crept in the ultimate result is illustrated on the lower half, which is the very next section to the reclaimed Bramley orchard.

Such a site, ideal in its freedom from frost, is worth reclaiming, but it takes a brave and energetic man to set about it.

Although fruitgrowers in England suffered at irregular intervals from Spring frosts, no general or practical interest in the matter was taken until after the May frost of 1935 had caused such widespread havoc all over the country that some investigation of frost and the possibility of controlling it seemed vital to the industry.

At a meeting of fruitgrowers convened at East Malling Research Station on 11 September, 1935, it became obvious that very little was known and understood about Spring frosts, although considerable literature on the subject was available from American sources where orchard heating was practised many years before any attempt was made to introduce it to this country. A comprehensive Bulletin entitled *Frost and the Prevention of Frost Damage* was issued by the U.S. Department of Agriculture in April, 1929, and revised and re-issued in 1940.

The study of frost by the amateur does not necessarily require any apparatus unless his eyesight needs the assistance of spectacles. Even thermometers are quite unnecessary, for, while they will record the temperature at any particular spot, they are unable to give a reason why that temperature is occurring and since quite considerable variations of temperature can be recorded by stations set at a few feet from each other (see graph on p. 33) the thermometer should only be necessary where confirmation of one's own expectations are required.

Granted the ability to observe, it should be possible after a few years' experience for the grower who has watched frost behaviour to say, " Here I can plant in safety. Here I shall be out of minor frosts but liable to inundation by major frosts, and here I should be crazy to plant anything at all."

Orchard heating, or the need for it, is an admission of bad

judgement in the choice of a site, or due to bad lay-out of the orchard in refusing to allow free drainage of air as determined by the contours of the land. At the same time, orchards in low and frosty places are often set on such good land and have attained such productive status that they may well justify the cost of orchard heating even on the most extensive scale.

2

Orchard heating on cordon apple orchard in Bedfordshire, 1938. Individual trees can be distinguished.

Photo: Biggleswade Chronicle

A Cotswold village, snugly placed, but in a frost-hole. When photographed in June, 1941, the walnuts were still leafless.

3

HOW FROSTS DEVELOP AND WHY

WE in Britain are not concerned with winter frosts, although these can occasionally cause no little damage to certain fruit trees. By the formation of ice beneath the bark, and consequent thawing, splitting of the bark may be caused with consequent drying out of the sap wood beneath leaving unsightly loose bark. Such damage occurred in the zero frosts of the early war years. Though such low temperatures are usually accompanied by radiation frost conditions, a general low temperature prevails over very large areas. Moderate Spring frosts, which can injure our fruit blossoms, are often quite local in incidence and may be of very short duration.

Really damaging Spring frosts are not casual happenings like thunderstorms, hail and lightning, which are all local disturbances. They are brewed by Dame Nature with ingredients brought literally from the ends of the earth. When the winds of April and May blow keenly from a quarter between the north-west and east day after day the stage is set and the performance may begin at any minute. The late Sir Napier Shaw, the noted meteorologist, formulated the theory that in April or thereabouts some three and a half billion tons of cold air move southwards from the Arctic regions. How do they affect us?

A high barometer reading may indicate the presence to the north-west or north-east of us of an anticyclone caused by the pressure of icy air from the Polar or Scandinavian regions forcing its way below air which is less cold. As a result of this incessant pressure a huge volume of the not-so-cold air is raised upwards and spreads outwards and eventually downwards on to us. Though to the Icelander it may be a pleasant Spring day, when this air reaches us we complain bitterly of unseasonable weather and hurry back into our winter woollies.

When in addition to an anticyclonic area in Scandinavia a persistent low pressure system happens to be sitting in the Bay of Biscay, drawing the cold air over us, Heaven help the lowland grower if a Spring frost develops.

If the passage of those billions of tons of cold air postulated by Sir Napier Shaw begins in early April and is maintained at a moderate concentration, giving a gradual general rise in night temperatures, we are likely to enjoy a late Spring, and by the time blossom is out and falling further supplies of cold air need not come our way. Such was the Spring of 1943, with no damaging frost reading in the dangerous period and a full fruit crop as a result. If, however, the southward passage of cold air is held up or preceded by a warm spell in early April we may get an unseasonably rapid response by all vegetation, and the sudden replacement of that genial air by very cold conditions as was the case in May 1944 and again in 1945.

In the last-named year April opened with warm weather. In the second week after two moderate ground frosts on the 8th and 9th we ran into an unduly hot spell lasting till the 22nd, when severe radiation frosts on the 23rd and 24th took a heavy toll of fruit blossom. A brief spell of cool weather followed and then on the 29th to 30th of April a wind-borne frost with a gale and blizzard struck us, followed by more severe radiation frosts on May 1st and 2nd which completed the destruction. A week later temperatures were up again and England sweltered in summer weather from Spain or North Africa with the mercury rising to 80° and over in the shade.

It is not right on the basis of a year like 1945 to consider that nothing can be done to combat frost. We have to reckon on the usual and disregard the thousand to one risk. Our main enemy is the anticyclone in spring and not the depression.

Early ice movements in the North Atlantic may herald the formation of these Spring anticyclones, but always our weather at this time of the year is decided and controlled by the movement of cold air for ever insistent on forming the lowest air stratum.

This action on the part of cold air is no inexplicable mystery. It goes on by day and by night and is simply the response of chilled air to the law of gravity. Cold air is literally heavier than warm air since a given volume of air contracts as its temperature is lowered and fills a smaller space. Actually a cubic foot of air at 34° F. weighs 0·0806 lbs. while at 26° F. it weighs 0·0820 lbs. Cold water is also denser and heavier than hot water, and it is on this principle that the thermo-syphon system of radiator cooling on a motor-car works ; water heated by contact with the cylinder head rising, cooling a little, and urged on by fresh supplies of heated water falling through the radiator tubes where it is still further cooled by the blast of cold air over the cooling fins thus establishing a circulation which keeps the temperature of the whole contents of the radiator below boiling-point. In practice, the so-called system of " heat inversion," which takes place when orchard heating is in progress, follows the same principle, except that for " below boiling-point " one must write " above freezing-point."

Air is about a thousand times as light in weight as water, but both can be related in their behaviour if their relative weight and density are remembered. A cold current of water in less cold water will behave in much the same way as will a cold current of air in less cold air, except for the handicap imposed by weight.

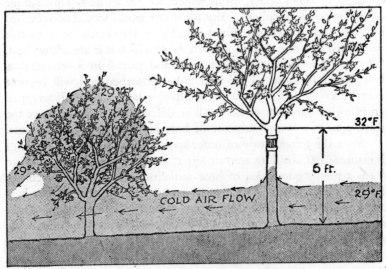

FIG. 1.—Showing how a flow of cold air meeting an obstacle will engulf it.

If we use water as comparable to air in order to illustrate the movements of cold air, then we should regard such movements as slow motion pictures which, compared with pictures projected at the normal speed, are familiar enough to all cinema audiences. If you will note how water running swiftly over a shallow stream bed will rise to engulf the small boulder, you may then visualise cold air moving slowly down a valley or gentle slope, rising and covering a fruit tree or bush which may be in its way. Where air drainage is considerable this actually happens, as is illustrated in Fig. 1, and Plate 13, facing page 49.

But to return to our anticyclone. If this persists, or if fresh anticyclones build up, a considerable period of chilly weather may be experienced. The longer the supply of cold air the greater the risk of a damaging frosty night. Since in Spring the surface of our section of the earth is still losing more heat during the nights than it is receiving from the sun during the shorter days, the loss of heat is increased by cold, dry winds from the north and east, and with these and a high barometer reading clear skys are almost certain to occur at night.

The loss of heat resulting in frost is related to the frightful coldness of outer space, from which we are protected to a large extent by our atmosphere. But for it our world would be scorched by day and frozen by night. Imagine the earth as a marble suspended before a radiant gas-fire, from which it is absorbing heat. When well warmed up, if removed and placed in a refrigerator, it will rapidly loose all the heat it has absorbed and will become very cold. If, however, the marble having been warmed is wrapped up in a cloth, its loss of heat will be delayed and reduced since the cloth acts as a non-conductor of heat and reduces radiation loss.

Since the temperature of outer space in which our earth swings is estimated at absolute zero or 273·1° of frost, Centigrade, you can form a pretty good idea of how radiation loss at night affects us. By day we are warmed up, but by night we must give up our heat and cool down, protected only from serious loss by our atmosphere and by such warmth as we have received during the day. We may, however, be wrapped up in cloud which will reduce our loss still more and, where conditions are favourable for a frost, only the presence of cloud or the springing up of a breeze will retard its development or reduce its severity.

Quite a moderate amount of cloud will prevent the development of a frost or bring one to an end, since the under surface of a cloud acts as a reflector, throwing back the heat rays to earth again in much the same way that a mirror will reflect sunlight.

Loss of heat by radiation is the primary cause of frost damage to fruit blossom in Spring, and the subject has some few complications which need clearing up.

It is a fact that every surface exposed to the clear unclouded sky during the night loses heat by radiation. The heat rays leaving the surface of any object, though they can neither be seen nor easily felt, travel outwards in straight lines in every direction. That this does occur is proved by the fact that if cloud is directly above the object B in Fig. 2, those rays which strike the cloud directly from below are reflected down again vertically, for in heat reflection as in light reflection " the angle of reflection is equal to the angle of incidence."

If, to a spectator, a cloud is half-way down towards the horizon, those heat rays which are leaving the object A in Fig. 2, vertically pass on outwards into space, but those which contact the under surface of the cloud, at say an angle of 45°, are reflected off again at approximately that angle and down to earth at a further point. The object which is losing heat vertically will receive a return of some of its own heat rays as well as heat rays from other distant

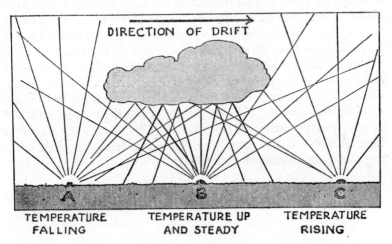

FIG. 2.—How a cloud dissipates a frost.

objects (such as C in Fig. 2) on the earth's surface, whose angle in relation to the cloud happens to reflect them to the particular area in which our object lies. This sounds rather complicated, but a diagram will make it clearer.

Cloud coming up when a radiation frost is beginning sends the temperature up surprisingly quickly. Its effect is noticeable on a thermometer long before it is over the observer, is at its greatest while the cloud is overhead, and fades as the cloud passes away to the horizon.

It may perhaps be simpler (though incorrect) to imagine any cloud in the sky, be it cirrus high up or nimbus down low, as absorbent of heat which is lost by the earth and able to retransmit it back again to the earth in greater or lesser degree. It will be obvious that the denser cloud near to the earth's surface will be able to distribute more heat than a gauzy whiff of cirrus cloud way up in the stratosphere.

Wind will also prevent frost developing on a radiation night by stirring up the air at soil-level, where frost mainly begins and preventing the collection of cold air in low places thus tending to preserve an even temperature. Wind and cloud therefore are two factors which prevent or reduce damaging spring frosts.

Soils may have some effect on local temperature but not enough to temper a major freeze. Water content which should have considerable effect is usually greatest at the lowest levels and so is rendered useless. Being exposed to the extremes of temperature its very small powers of cold reduction are hardly noticeable.

Hoar frost (see Plate 4, facing p. 16) will be deposited from the air on any cooled surface when the air is inclined to be moist and the dew-point is below freezing-point. The drier the air the lower the dew-point. Hoar frosts are just as common in Autumn as in Spring, but the old saw " three white frosts then a thaw " is not always correct. The peculiar phenomenon illustrated in Plate 4, which is the result of a November frost, occurred when fog and frost combined their efforts.

CHAPTER IV

THE BEHAVIOUR OF COLD AIR

COLD air and hot air share a strange similarity in their behaviour. Both hold with the utmost tenacity to that position which gravity has decreed for them.

In considering the behaviour of cold air it will be helpful to get a general idea of how air at differing temperatures behaves. Cold air and hot air, curiously enough, behave exactly alike but in opposed directions. Cold air falls but hot air rises. Cold air contracts, hot air expands.

Open the door of a refrigerator and cold air slips out and down to the floor. Open the gas oven and out and up rushes a blast of hot air. Both these are extremes of performance in a moderate temperature, and the speed of currents of cold air or hot air is controlled by the temperature of the air in which they move. For example, hot air will rise slowly in air which is warm because its difference in weight compared with that of the air through which it rises is slight. Hot air rising through cold air will move quickly because it is being forced on by the insistent pressure of the heavier cold air anxious to take its place. From this it will be realised that the general air temperature of the atmosphere just above the soil will have a tremendous effect on the motion of cold air formed at soil-level which is moving away to find its lowest possible resting place. Indeed movement of air at ground-level is entirely controlled by the temperature of air higher up. No variation means no movement. Great variation means rapid movement. Air movement is greatly affected by the surface over which it moves. Gales at sea are more severe than on land because there are no obstructions above sea-level to break the force of the wind. Slow moving cold air currents will move more swiftly over a smooth macadam road than across a rough grass field. In that case the grass exerts a braking effect, and until the cold air current has overlapped the grass drainage to lower levels will not begin. Having reached the level of the top of the grass movement of the current will continue, but beneath the added depth of cold air the grass will lose more heat by radiation than before and this will be recorded by a thermometer laid on the grass.

Cold air and warm air are very unwilling to mix and to induce

them to do so at all it is necessary to stir them up thoroughly
with wind or by applied heat.

For curiosity during the summer of 1937, from August 7 to
August 13, I set two thermographs, or recording thermometers,
running. One stood in my office exposed to the temperature
within a thin, wooden building under a corrugated iron roof. The
second stood three feet above the floor of my cellar which was
entirely below ground-level, had an open door reached by outside
steps, and windows below gratings set on two sides of it, all being
open.

During the whole period of the trial the cellar thermograph
stood at 60° F. except for a brief period during one night when it
fell to 58° F. The thermograph in the office showed that the
temperature there averaged as high as 70° F., once reached 95° F.
and only once fell to 58° F.

The natural inference must be that in the case of air chilled
to several degrees below the air in its neighbourhood and sheltered
from direct sunlight, there is little inclination for heat exchange
between the two and they may almost be regarded as separate
entities.

It is very easy to relate small movements of chilled air to large
movements, as their behaviour is exactly the same, one has only
to sit near a large shut window on a night when the temperature
is falling rapidly owing to radiation loss to realise that an extremely
cold draught is falling to the floor and encouraging one's chilblains
to vigorous protest.[1] Exactly the same effect on a major scale is
produced on the rock-faces of some of the Norwegian mountains,
where, when sunset has been passed and full radiation is developing,
the rock-face chills rapidly and really violent winds pour downwards
to the fiords below.

Failure to realise this air-drainage theory is said to have been
the cause of the loss of the Scott expedition, which chose the
presumably more sheltered valleys in preference to the obviously
exposed high levels which Amundsen favoured. In those natural
gulleys terribly low temperatures and persistent winds made life
almost impossible. Amundsen, wiser in his choice of routes,
succeeded because he chose the higher lands and avoided the worst

[1] Indeed, it may be a liberal education to the uninitiated to take a few living-room
temperature readings, when, on a chilly night with a good fire burning, the temperature near the ceiling will be found very different from that near the floor, especially
by the door or the window.

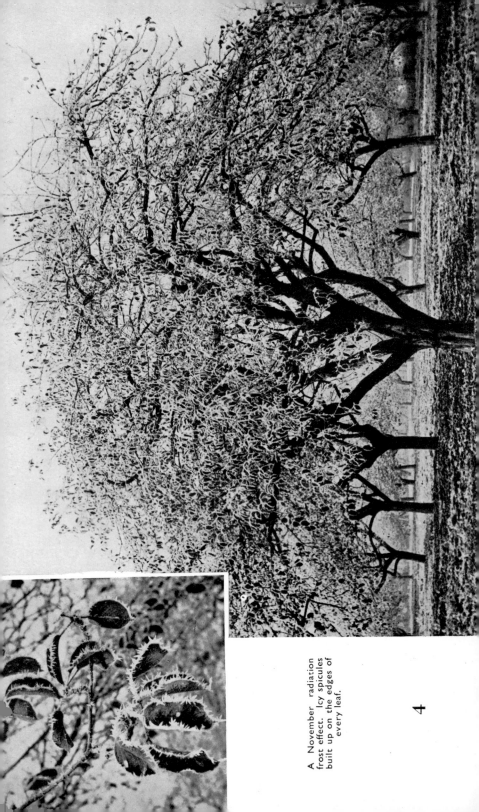

A November radiation frost effect. Icy spicules built up on the edges of every leaf.

4

Cloud developing from high vapour trail left by one aeroplane. Date, early pink-bud stage.

Taken June 6, 1941, on the road between Billingshurst and Wisborough Green, showing oaks on slope in full leaf while those 30 ft. below in the valley bottom were completely leafless.

5

effects of cold-air drainage. Be that as it may, it has been reported again and again that from the face of the great ice barrier violent draughts of icy air pour from those levels which provide drainage-flows so that there should have been adequate information available on which to determine a sound choice of route.

Referring back to the consistent low temperature of the cellar, a most interesting observation was issued in 1934 by Dr. Wilhelm Schmidt, of the Central Meteorological Institute, Vienna. Some 1,270 metres above sea-level, in the Austrian mountains, lies a perfect cup, or frost-hole, in which the protection afforded by the surrounding mountains prevents the disturbance of the air by wind in exactly the same way that protection was afforded to my cellar. Now note the results of this. Neither in the lowest nor the highest parts of Austria was so low a temperature recorded on radiation nights as in this frost-hole, indeed, the author stated that probably they were the lowest in the whole of Europe, excluding only the most northerly and easterly parts. At the bottom of this cup grew grasses of the same type as are found in the far north of Siberia, but no trees.

The author writes :

The formation of this temperature distribution is obvious ; on clear nights the outgoing radiation at these higher levels, especially strong during anti-cyclonic weather, cools the slopes and the contiguous air ; this air flows down and collects at the bottom, forming a pond of cold air. Its surface rises gradually until it reaches the pass of Lechnergraben, some 50 metres above the level of the bottom of the cup. Then it flows over the edge like water over a weir.

So much for what happens at night. In daytime, unlike the cellar which is shielded from the sun, this cup in the Austrian mountains had its full share of sun heat and warmed up accordingly, but as a frost-hole it remains a classic example of cold-air behaviour when radiation loss is at work.

This particular frost-hole is of comparatively small area, merely a matter of acres, now let us compare it with one of our South of England major frost-holes.

From Edenbridge through Tonbridge, Marden, Headcorn and almost to Pluckley, a distance of 25 miles or so, the Southern Railway runs in a straight line through a stretch of country with high hills to North and South of it. To the West lie the line of the Surrey hills above Dorking, Reigate and Redhill ; there is also the high range, on the North side of which lies Sevenoaks. To the

East and North-east the range of the North Downs rises more than 500 feet above the valley bottom.

This narrow stretch of plain, 25 miles long by an average of 5 miles across, has no outlet for the cold air which drains into it from areas a considerable distance away, save the narrow exit provided by the upper reaches of the Medway; and during the last 5 miles, until Maidstone is reached, this becomes very restricted and is liable to further additions of cold air from the Bearsted direction.

Save for this one outlet by Maidstone there is no overflow possible in any direction except in the South-east, and then only when the pooling cold air has risen to a depth of more than 50 feet above the average level of the valley floor. On an area of over 100 square miles a fifty-foot rise is not hard to come by, and around Marden and Staplehurst there are several rises which should escape any but the very worst frosts, while the hill-sides near Paddock Wood and Brenchley hold many safe sites. One such site in the former area has cropped with remarkable consistency above a definite level even in the bad frost years.

These land-locked frost-holes of great size are not common though the area in which lie Wisboro Green and Kirdford is in an even worse category than the Marden district, here the contours are very complicated and involve practically the whole of the land drained by the Rivers Arun and Rother. With higher land in every direction and the natural outlet to the sea in the South blocked by the great range of the South Downs, the half-mile wide gap at Amberley cannot begin to cope with the pooling flood of cold air. As a result the frost-level rises and rises during major frosts until well over the hundred-foot level of submergence is reached on the low lands, with terribly low temperatures as a result.

The student of frost who buys Bartholomew's half-inch to the mile maps in colour can see for himself in any county where these large land-locked frost-holes lie. What he cannot see are the thousands of small individual frost-holes and safe places which exist and to which he must apply some formula similar to the one I have advised in Chapter 9 if he is to choose a safe site on which to plant fruit.

The only case which has been brought to my notice of anyone taking advantage of cold-air flows is the method used by the natives of Manchuria in storing their persimmon fruits. I have not the reference which I believe appeared in the *American Geographical Magazine*.

At the bottom of a deep gorge beside a river, wide level flats were ridged up by the natives in much the same way that a field is prepared for potato planting. Across the tops of the deep furrows bamboo poles were laid and covered with mats. The persimmons were laid out several thicknesses deep and covered over with more mats. During radiation nights, common enough in the Manchurian autumn, extremely cold air gravitated to the river level and submerged the beds of stored persimmons, flowing over and under the fruits along the trenches beneath the bamboo poles and mats. As a result of this cold-air flow the fruits fell to a low temperature which was well maintained against the sun heat of the day aided by the insulation of the mats above, and the chilled soil beneath.

There is no reason why anyone who wishes to make use of cold-air flows for the storage of hard fruit, such as apples and pears, should not take advantage of an obvious drainage channel and arrange a cold store, so that during the night cold air can be allowed to flow into and through the store cooling the whole interior and its contents down to a usefully low level. Once cooled, the store should be shut up until another night with a low temperature comes along to repeat the cooling-down. The idea would pre-suppose the building of the store mainly below soil-level so that cold air once collected would stay put, and in order to take full advantage of the great insulation against loss of cold so gained which earth provides.

One other example can be recorded. This was the deliberate planting up of a frost-hole by an East Anglian nurseryman, who said that he was thereby saved the trouble of de-blossoming his young fruit trees. The reason may have seemed a sound one, but in a bad frost, nursery stock which is planted in a frosty situation can receive a severe check from a keen Spring frost losing valuable time in making a recovery.

CHAPTER V

HOW PLANTING METHODS MAY INVITE FROST

THE bush tree on the dwarfing stock (as distinct from the standard tree on the crab or free stock) has been very generally planted in England during the past thirty years (see Fig. 1). It is met with on the Continent, but the Americans have as yet seen no sound reason in it to induce them to alter their methods.

Dwarf trees have suited the nurserymen admirably, for instead of planting some 27 standard trees to the acre at 40 feet apart, the fruit-grower had been persuaded to crowd as many bush trees as 302 to the acre at 12 feet apart. Indeed, when he could be persuaded to plant on the Equilateral Triangle system 348 trees could be set to the acre! Where cordon apples are planted at 2 feet apart and 6 feet between the rows, 3,630 trees can be planted on an acre of ground. The greatest known concentration is in Hertfordshire, where one grower has set his trees at 1 foot apart in rows 3 feet apart, 14,520 trees to the acre!

Not satisfied with this, all manner of soft fruit crops were at one time recommended as intercrops to bring a swift cash return (see Plate XX), so that the wretched trees struggled for light, grew upright, lost their lower fruit spurs for lack of sun and in a few years were growing into one another.

When this happened, usually about the ninth or tenth year after planting, the grower was advised to grub out his diagonal rows, leaving his permanent plant at about 17 feet apart. That was feasible if he had planted on the square system, but was a very much more drastic operation if planted on the triangular system.

In many cases where this grubbing has been done, growers have found that after smaller crops for two years their record crop to date has come by the third year, clearly suggesting that wider planting in the first instance would have produced much larger crops earlier still. In the meantime by close planting the grower believes he has harvested his maximum possible weight from his acreage. I think that he is, in most cases, very much mistaken.

We have seen in Chapter I that our English variation in crop is 298 per cent. as against an American variation of 30 per cent. Is this due entirely to the fact that we have in many cases disregarded the lie of the land and planted in frost-holes? I think not. Much of the variation is due to overclose planting, which, apart from light, water and nutritional needs, denies free and rapid air drainage and predisposes orchards to unnecessary and avoidable frost damage which persistently reduces cropping.

Of all planting systems for use on a site where the fall of the land is gentle and in one direction, and where there is a large area of higher land behind, the triangular plant is the most dangerous. It is seldom, if ever, used to-day, but where, as is the case in many elderly orchards, trees were cut low to induce branch formation from near soil-level, then one only needs a good stand of perennial weed or neglected tussock grass around the base of the tree and a few leaves on the tree itself to provide a complete block against air drainage.

If, on the other hand, the plant is on the square system with the trees set so that they run with the lie of the land, then every row is a natural air-drainage channel.

Where closely planted trees on the square or triangular system are neglected and are allowed to go down to deep, uncut weed, frost damage may occur even on good sites. Clean cultivation in the Spring is an aid to air drainage and should not be omitted, except where orchards are grassed down. In the latter case the grass should be kept cut or short grazed.

The most dwarf systems of fruit-growing, the dwarf pyramid and the cordon, need very careful placing if they are to escape frost. There are hundreds of acres of cordon apples planted on useful sites across the line of fall of the land thus checking all air movement on radiation frost nights until the collected cold air has overtopped them. Planted in rows running in line with the landfall they would pass nearly all the cold air and lose only the lowest blossoms through frost.

In many places air drainage would function efficiently if standard or half-standard trees were grown in place of the low-branching bush trees, for the draining cold air would be too shallow to make contact with the main mass of the tree (Fig. 1).

Suppose that you have an orchard of bush trees running down into a frosty valley bottom which carries a regular cold-air drainage flow ? If the last few rows of trees are even one-third submerged in a cold-air current, what happens ? The cold-air current on meeting the obstructing tree swirls up in slow motion into the main branch system to fall away again on the lower side of it to rejoin the main air flow. This upward flow and saturation of the tree is maintained while the frost lasts and cold air continues to drain away at a level involving the lowest branches.

If radiation is intense the localised lowering of temperature in and around the tree will destroy or damage its blossom. Yet, a few yards away, a tree which, having a few added feet of elevation, is out of the main depth of the cold-air flow will escape entirely. The photographs on Plate 13 show a well-laden Cox which stood no higher up the valley-side than four feet, yet its neighbour standing those few feet lower down was stripped by frost from bottom to top. Notice, that this was not a case of wholesale submergence by pooled cold air but of a cold air-drift rising as it met a sufficient obstruction in just the same way that water in a shallow, swift-moving stream will rise and cover a projecting boulder.

If the reader can visualise such air behaviour by the obvious after-results he will begin to realise how close planting can induce frost and why some places would be better set out to tall-stemmed standard trees than to short-stemmed bush trees. (Fig. 3.)

The Americans, wiser in their generation, set their trees far apart planting half-standard rather than standard (which latter were really only designed so that stock could be grazed beneath the trees at such time as they were not bowed down with fruit), and allowed the natural habit of the tree full development. With what result? Magnificent growth. Branches spread outwards almost horizontally and a tremendous crop-carrying capacity resulted. Wide-angled branches can carry great crops, for as every fruitgrower knows while the acute V-angled branch means easy breakage under even a small crop the right-angled branch will carry the crop and a man's weight as well. The Americans neglect no opportunities and it would, I think, be fatuous on our part to imagine that they would not long ago have adopted our dwarf tree had they not picked bigger and better crops under their own system of planting.

There is a move to-day in the direction of wider planting. In 1936, on a well-sited farm, I advised planting Cox on Type 2, as bush trees at 18 feet apart with nothing planted in between. In 1944 those trees were carrying some six hundred and forty bushels of apples to the acre (over 11 tons 8 cwt.) but had already begun to meet in the row. My recommendation for 1944-5 season planting on this good soil is 24 feet apart for Cox, as bushes on Type 2 stock, with no interplanting with fillers or anything else save the abominable potato crop which the War Agricultural

Committee still makes the grower plant. In 1952 those trees should be worth seeing.

It shocks me to see the old scramble to put in as many trees to the acre as possible. Close planting means more initial expense, more labour, less ease in cultivation and spraying, more scab, poor tree growth and with every added season a greater liability to frost. Wider planting has everything in its favour except the early return from precocious fillers, an asset which is undoubtedly offset in the long run by bigger and finer crops from the permanent trees and every cultural advantage.

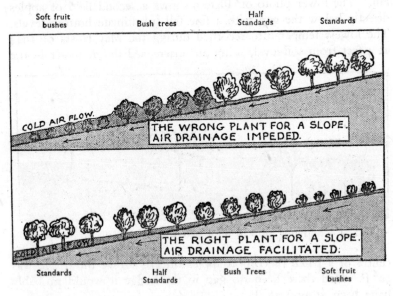

FIG. 3.

If every twig of a tree is entitled to full light, and if pruning is conducted rationally on modern methods (and for most apples Mr. C. R. Thompson's system is excellent—*Modern Apple Tree Pruning.* Headley Bros., London, 2s.) then one should plant a tree which will grow to 12 feet in height at 24 feet from its neighbour. I believe that to be a sound planting allowance—double the height to determine the planting distance—for most fruits and have little doubt that even cordon apple and pear rows, which reach 6 feet in height and are usually allowed no more than that between the rows, would benefit by being 12 feet between the rows; nor do I expect that there would be any considerable decrease in weight to outweigh the advantages of better quality and crop and greatly increased convenience in culture.

In Chapter XI I have mentioned the danger of high hedges but, where there is adequate fall provided gaps are cut in strategic positions through high hedges, the danger vanishes, since a sizeable gap will pass a deal of cold-air drainage and will have a good effect in drawing off cold air from the surrounding area.

The upper photo on Plate 9 shows such a hedge, mainly stout hawthorn, backed with young lime trees, and set across an easy fall. The lower photo on Plate 9 shows a second field of apples directly below the gap with a fine fall to ultimate bottom levels. The lowest temperature recorded during the May frosts of 1944 at 4 feet from soil-level, using an unscreened thermometer in the

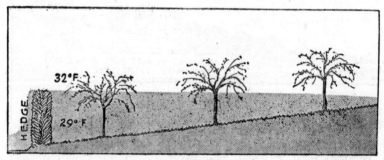

Fig. 4.—Showing how a high hedge can back up air drainage

centre of a patch of cordon apples directly above the hedge was 30° F. Had there been no gap in the hedge it would probably have been around 26° F.

Now, suppose that a field on a nice gentle slope has tall hedges on both sides and a twenty-foot hedge-cum-windbreak at the bottom. On a radiation night, no matter at what height above sea-level, cold air would drain down the slope and begin to collect behind and above this bottom hedge and, even though a proportion of the cold air found its way through the hedge, enough depth would build-up and back-up to engulf a considerable portion of the lower half of the orchard (Fig. 4). Beneath that banked-up cold air radiation loss would be intensified and a really low temperature would soon be forthcoming.

By all means plant, maintain and grow tall, dense hedges as

6

Contours which collect and guide cold air flows above the screen shown below.

View of screen from the hill.

A fifty-foot section of Bugge's heater system on a Sussex orchard with hop-screening on lower side of hedge.

Orchard-heater pots laid out ready to light in a Surrey orchard.

Looking up the orchard. Note high hedges at side and across the line of fall.

7

shelter belts, provided they are set in line with the fall of the land. Also, if you wish, provide windbreaks across the line of fall provided that these are not planted too close together and are kept clear of lower branches and the grass below is kept cut. Under such windbreaks as are shown on Plate 10 air movement is not materially impeded and no build-up of cold air will take place. But if dense high hedges are grown upon all sides of a plantation of dwarf apples on a gently sloping site the best method of preventing frost damage will be to borrow a bull-dozer and rip out plenty of wide gaps in the hedges which cross the slope.

CHAPTER VI

HOW WATER PLAYS A PART IN FROST

IT is obvious that water, probably standing at a temperature well above 50° F. on a May night of radiation frost, will have some local effect on the temperature of air in contact with it. Directly, this effect is very slight indeed, but indirectly it may be considerable.

It has been suggested that that nearness to water prevents frost, but it is difficult to see how this can be unless the surface area of the water is considerable. Anyone who has inadvertently bathed in the sea off the high cliffs of Devon on a clear radiation night in November will probably have been struck by the warmness of the water compared with the extreme cold of the air coming down on to it from the land.

The observant student of frost may have noticed, after a night of major frost (or even of medium frosts such as those of May 7 to 10, 1944, and again in early May 1945), that a familiar water plant such as Arrowhead, growing in shallow water and at that time of the year some six inches above the surface, will be completely frosted and brown if the pond in which it is growing happens to be in a reception area or frost-hole.

Now had the water (obviously standing above freezing-point) been able to put up any considerable amount of warmth as a protective envelope sufficient in depth to cover a plant of this sort no frost damage should have been forthcoming. This does not happen.

Water loses heat by radiation slowly and its major part on a frosty night is to provide a condition of local inertia. In itself it produces no cold air, but it does provide an excellent frictionless surface over which cold air can travel.

If the cold air draining down on to a large expanse of water is the drainage from a moderate or small area of land, then, since the water is producing no cold air, it allows for the rapid spread across its surface of the cold-air drainage with a consequent lowering of the general depth to which cold air can pool or collect at its level in its immediate neighbourhood.

It is for this reason that land close to the sea or near wide estuaries is comparatively frost-free, the flows of chilled air from the higher land spread rapidly across its level surface.

Where shallow valley-sides run down to wide rivers frost may seldom accumulate to a damaging depth since it has a fine frost-free surface over which to spread and in some cases the fall of the river is enough to ensure that as cold air is formed and drains on to its surface it moves away from the neighbourhood which is generating it.

Occasionally, as an example of true micro-climatology, one can trace in winter where very local air drainage is directed to a definite spot or to one side of a pond, with the result that freezing over begins there long before the rest of the surface freezes.

In Hatfield Park, some years ago the planting of fruit was proposed in the old garden by the River Lea where Queen Elizabeth used to walk. As this site lay between steep slopes I suggested that a few thermometer readings in Spring would be a useful guide as to suitability.

In this case we had an obvious frost-hole, but the pooling area was a wide water surface stretching about a mile with a fall to lower country. The steep slopes were of no great area though there was a likelihood of air drainage coming in from a larger area outside.

The thermometer readings showed that while very cold air-drainage currents ran in their expected channels to the water below, they spread out there and became so shallow above the wide stretch of water that the garden by the waterside stood at a higher temperature than the drainage channels on the slopes above. The water in this case was able to look after anything but a major frost.

Water, then, can be regarded as a frost-free section so far as the production of cold air is concerned, and in estimating the possible build-up of cold air in an area which contains a large surface of water the area of the water can be deducted from the total. Thus if on a hundred acres of land comprising donor,[1] intermediate and recipient areas ten acres of water are present, then in a radiation frost cold air from no more than ninety acres is to be expected.

[1] These three types are defined in Chapter VIII.

CHAPTER VII

WHAT HAPPENS ON A FROSTY NIGHT?

WHEN the sun has set and radiation loss is beginning considerable air movements are taking place a few hundred feet above sea-level in country which is hilly. These air movements will reach a climax soon after sunset and will have subsided by the time darkness arrives. In the valleys and lower levels there is likely to be much moisture-laden air, and as this begins to chill, part of the moisture must be thrown out as dew since the amount of moisture which can be contained in air is related to the temperature of the air. You will note, for example, that the cold tap in the steam-filled bathroom is the one upon which water condenses. In the same way dew or hoar-frost will develop on surfaces lower in temperature than the air.

Already from the higher land cooler air is persistently creeping in below this warmer air to take its place. On the long southern slope of Bredon Hill in Worcestershire, for example, at sunset on any fine summer evening a cool breeze pours downwards in a steady stream which ceases only when the sun is well below the horizon and the valley and hill-side temperatures have evened up. On a clear but chilly day in May, this same evening breeze in a greater or lesser degree is preparing the way for a frost all over the countryside. As night proceeds a noticeable chill develops near the streams in the valley bottoms and plains since they are at the lowest levels. From them an accumulation of cold air extends and deepens. The plains themselves are developing a thin skin of cold air which will soon begin to collect and slide off from any slopes, rises or hillocks just as soon as enough extra weight has been given by cold and collection to allow gravity to operate. Where slopes are steep this " skin " of cold air being a fast feed is drawn thin ; where the landfall is gentle the skin thickens and drains more slowly, but it is doubtful if there is any motion suggestive of a loose formation or rolling masses of air. Where a feed of cold air is drained by a natural gulley on a slope the chilled air will only occupy that depth of the gulley needed to pass its quota, and the clear cut tide mark on such shoots as opening bracken fronds, and young ash-leaf will show exactly how deep the current of air was, provided of course that a frost low enough in temperature to damage either was able to develop.[1]

If the area of land draining into our gulley formation is large the gulley may pass a full bore of chilled air and become itself productive of air below freezing-point despite high elevation, a natural fall and an ultimate outlet. Modifications of this type of contour are common on hill-side orchards and damage will often occur in such localised formations (Fig. 5).

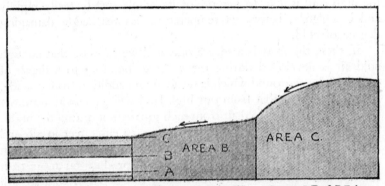

FROST HOLE   INTERMEDIATE   DONOR AREA

FIG. 5.—The level indicated by A shows how at the beginning of a frosty night cold air draining from Areas B and C collects in a frost-hole and helps to begin the formation of a damaging low temperature. Later in the progress of the frost the level of damaging cold air has risen to the level of line B. Air above this level and up to the line marked C show the amount of added cold air which has flowed down from the higher land above and pooled above the damaging frost level at B. Once the temperature of the pooling cold air has begun to get really low the air drainage from the higher land ceases to flow down to the lowest level of the frost-hole and forms a less cold stratum above it.

You have, therefore, on a frosty night three different sources from which come cold air. The hill-tops and well-drained ridges

[1] Bracken, when young, is scorched by frost. Drooping daffodils and narcissi indicate the passage of a very severe frost and were noticeable in 1938. Ash damages easily and though not quite so susceptible as walnut foliage, young ash shoots are completely shrivelled by a frost which hardly begins to blast the foliage of the beech or the oak. Sweet or Spanish Chestnut is about as tender as the ash. Where apples are grown near ash and oak trees, and the leaf is frosted but the oak is not blackened, a reasonable number of apples should mature. After the frosts of May 1944 and 1945, both of which entirely shrivelled a large walnut tree in my paddock, an apple tree within a few feet of it carried the heaviest crop of apples it had ever borne. Walnut is even more susceptible than ash to frost.

and hummocks from which cooled air pours on to the second source, the land which is less well drained and which has to pass in addition to its own supply that from higher levels. Both these must discharge upon the third source of cold air and the most prolific source, namely the lowest levels of all, valley bottoms, open plains and so forth. Plate 16, lower section, illustrates these contours.

Now all these levels, high, medium and low, are themselves losing heat by radiation and are producing chilled air, but only the high land is able to get rid of its whole supply really rapidly and completely, before its temperature has reached a damaging degree of cold.

If, then, the frost is a severe one, and we suppose that enough cold air is developed during the night to build-up to a depth of 10 feet on level ground which is receiving no addition from outside, it will be realised that from our high land will pass away no more than 10 cubic feet of cold air from each square foot during the night. Our medium land may then have to pass 20 cubic feet in all, and our bottom land will have to add this twenty to its own contribution of ten (in practice the bottom land would produce far more than high or medium levels). At least thirty feet depth of cold air will in theory, therefore, lie over the bottom collecting area.

If, instead of a foot you take a square mile or ten square miles as your receiving area and surround it with five times as much higher land, then add up your cold-air deposits, it will be realised that the depth of cold air pooling in a valley or over a level plain may be very considerable.

Of these three sources, high, medium and low, the air from the highest land is the least cold. It is formed around ground-level from air at a temperature which remains comparatively warm. Its fall to lower levels therefore begins long before freezing-point is reached (which explains why potato leaves on a well-sited hill-side may be quite undamaged by a frost which plays havoc with valley crops) and before any considerable concentration of chilled air has developed and its flow continues without any real depth having been reached.

The land taking the flows of cold air and passing them on to the lowest levels must of necessity be burdened with its own production of chilled air, and it is on these intermediate levels that we have the strangely uneven responses to damage by those trees which respond to it—the natural frost thermographs. Such damage is undoubtedly caused by or made possible by cold-air currents of varying depths pursuing their devious ways to the pooling area. When we arrive at that last level the tidemark of a lake of cold air following a major spring frost is indicated by damage to a uniform depth indicated by blackened ash, oak and walnut and by browned beech. This tidemark does not indicate anything like the full amount of collected chilled air but it does indicate the depth of the stratum of cold air at a temperature low enough to cause such damage.

It would seem that since air movement is taking place from the higher levels at temperatures which are not damaging to tender varieties of plant as, for instance, the potato, that a great deal of comparatively warm air must be finding its way downhill. This can be so up to a point, which point is decided by the difference in temperature and weight of the hill-side air at soil-level and the air just above. While it is mainly in the lowest levels that damaging frost develops, that frost is not transferred as frost from the average high levels except where land contours favour the formation of persistent air-drainage currents. Leaf and other surfaces submerged in chilled air at the lowest levels, or in these air currents on the intermediate levels, lose their heat very rapidly since there is no surrounding warm air to offset the radiation loss, as is the case higher up.

Very few upland sites can of themselves generate enough cold air to cause damage to top-fruit trees, such as apples, pears and plums and cherries. On any but flat land the initial chill which will develop into damage must come from land which is higher up.

The amount of cold air which various densities of tree and woodland can provide by radiation is very small indeed compared with arable or grass land. A large wood can be considered as non-productive of cold air, since it so shelters the ground beneath that no radiation loss of any consequence is possible. But a large wood which stands in the path of a cold-air feed will suck up and hold a great deal of cold air to the damage of its foliage and young shoots. Young, open coppices will hold up air drainage and allow a build-up of damaging cold air which is clearly visible where young ash or the susceptible sweet chestnut is growing.

So we may have vegetation at say 250 feet above sea-level losing heat at no lower temperature than a steady 34° F., while similar vegetation in the valley below at 100 feet above sea-level is dropping in temperature from 32° F. to 24° F. in a few hours. Provided the contours and site favour it you can duplicate the same figures in a matter of thirty feet difference in height or even less. It is the cold-air drainage and collection from the upper levels of land which make the low temperatures of the bottom lands possible and which speed up its low temperature development.

If these air movements can be visualised it will be admitted readily that for records to be of any value the position in which to place a recording thermometer must be chosen with great care. There will be positions on up-and-down lands within a few feet of each other where the temperature will vary considerably. A thermometer set at 3 feet above the ground may be well above the level of a shallow cold-air stream, while in another place at 6 feet above ground it may be submerged in a persistent current of equally cold air caused by the lie of the land.[1]

In practice, even where the whole area is submerged in cold air which has pooled to a great depth, any raised site in that area which offers a three-or four-way fall to the lowest level will record a slightly higher temperature than the level land, since the tendency is for the coldest air to always drain away downhill.

In considering the three types of site—high, medium and low— it will be noted that even in a severe radiation frost crops growing on the highest sites may escape all damage. Such crops are fully exposed to radiation loss, but this is continually conterbalanced by the surrounding air temperature and all that happens is a steady production of slightly cooled air which continually moves off downhill, becoming involved during its passage with colder air currents.

As an example of this difference in hill-top and bottom land temperature a reading taken at 520 feet up on the hills above Blackmoor in Hants gave on 19 April, 1939, which was not a bad frost year, a temperature of 32° F. During the same night the minimum reading at 300 feet was 25° F., or seven degrees below freezing, while on a site at between 400 and 500 feet, which, having a two-way fall, drained extremely well, the temperature never fell below 35° F., three degrees above freezing-point. These figures are indicative of the futility of placing thermometers at random, since obviously the top thermometer was placed in a site where drainage of air was slow, and although the cold air could not be

[1] On 24 April, 1945, I visited the land illustrated by the upper of the two graphs on opposite page. On the upper levels the lowest recorded temperature of the previous night and early morning at 4 feet above ground was 30° F., and no blossom was damaged. Below in the meadows the apple blossom was browned by the frost which at 7 feet above ground had been 24° F.

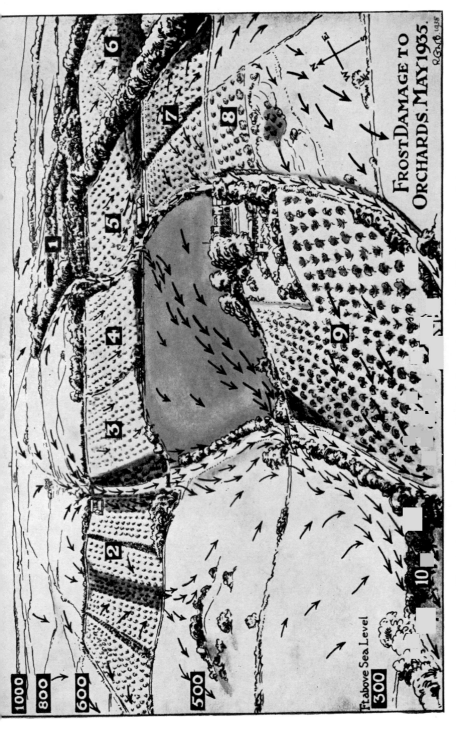

FROST DAMAGE TO ORCHARDS. MAY 1935.

Ft. above Sea Level

How land contours can direct cold air drainage, thus causing localised damage to fruit crops.

8

Gap cut in high
shelter hedge to allow
air drainage from
higher land on right.

The orchard directly
below the gap with
a fall of 200 ft. to
valley bottom.

9

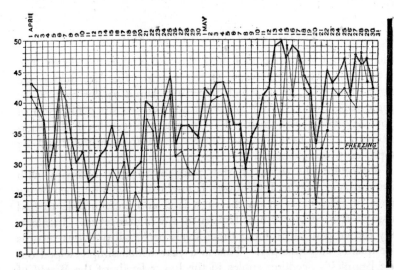

The heavy graph line indicates minimum night temperatures in degrees Fahrenheit on an orchard at 520 feet elevation during April and May 1938. The light line indicates corresponding temperatures at valley bottom (300 feet) level of the same Hampshire hillside. (Recorded on the Blackmoor Estate, Liss, Hants.)

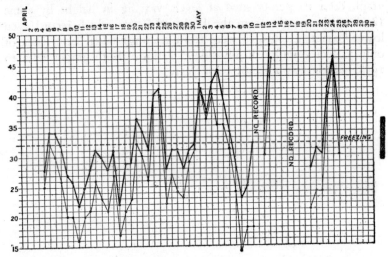

The light graph line indicates minimum night temperatures in a shallow valley about 250 feet above sea-level at 3 feet above soil. The heavy line indicates corresponding temperatures also at 3 feet above soil but only 31 feet higher up the hillside, clearly indicating the passage of a steady flow of extremely cold drainage air. (Recorded on the Leckford Estate, Stockbridge, Hants.)

The black line on the right-hand side shows the comparative distances between top and bottom thermometer stations.

said to pool its movement was sluggish and some depth had developed. The temperature at the 300–400 feet site during the night of 15 May, 1941, which wiped out about 75 per cent of the home fruit crop only fell to 30° F., and on this site a full crop of Cox developed and matured. On the 300-feet level the thermometer fell to 17° F., fifteen degrees below freezing-point and the apple crop was wiped out.

Following the frosts of May 7 to 10, 1944, in company with the manager of the Blackmoor Estate fruit, we examined many acres of fruit blossom on the high land and were unable to find a single frosted blossom or fruitlet on the higher levels. Incidentally the crop of all fruits at these levels broke all previous records for quality and quantity. This in a year which simply wiped out the Bramley's Seedling apples in the lower levels of the Weald of Kent.

The graphs on previous page show the degree of temperature variation which may be expected at varying levels on a hill-side as compared with a valley bottom. While those on the Blackmoor graph refer to points sited at levels varying in height by some 180 feet, the graphs from the Leckford Estate which record even lower base temperatures were from readings taken from sites of only 31 feet variation in hill-side elevation. Both graphs refer to 1938, which was a major frost year.

CHAPTER VIII

HOW LAND CONTOURS AFFECT AIR DRAINAGE

SOME study of land contours in relation to cold air is vitally necessary to the fruitgrower. Much time and money may be lost by neglect of this as the following instance will serve to show.

In 1938, after the May frost, I was asked to pass the final verdict on a small orchard of fruit set out in 1936 and now, according to the owner, badly frosted. As the orchard lay almost at the bottom of a valley several miles long, of less than a half-mile width at the bottom, and backed by steep sides which rose over the two-hundred-foot level, it was certain to be a frost-hole. Added to that a restricted outlet towards its drainage end made pooling of cold air to a great depth absolutely certain. I advised the grower to dig up his trees while yet young enough to move easily, and to seek higher levels. This particular grower had some years before asked me to vet a site for him in another county which I had reported upon as excellent, yet having bought the land he decided that he did not care for the district or the neighbours, sold his farm and planted up a perfect frost-hole.

The saucer-shaped depression on the level plain is the simplest type of frost-hole. It fills by slow drainage as do the lower levels of the wide valleys. Cold air pools in both to the depth of their possible discharge level (see Fig. 6, overleaf). If the lower slopes have large areas of high land behind and above them, and are not steep enough to speed drainage of air, they may suffer considerably from frost, especially if high hedges or belts of trees are set across the line of fall thus hindering or backing-up the air flows.

One can differentiate to some extent between sites by defining them as donor or recipient areas. A true donor area is one which allows the rapid fall in one or more directions of all the chilled air which it produces. A recipient area is one which must accept all the cold air which drains on to it from a donor area. Thus, a hillock set in the middle of a plain is a donor area and the plain a recipient area, but in many cases fruit farms are set between the two, and it is in the intermediate areas of air drainage from donor to recipient that most of the difficult problems of assessing safety from frost are to be met.

Only if an intermediate area is capable of discharging its own supply of chilled air in addition to such cold airs as flow on to it from its donor areas can a site within the area be regarded as a safe one. As an example of this, a valley near the coast, taking cold air from its hill-sides and having a good fall to the sea, may be perfectly safe provided that the valley bottom is wide, the fall is good and the hill-sides are not unduly high. Of all recipient areas the sea is the finest since it is the ultimate objective of all cold-air

FIG. 6.—Visual estimation of frost risks. The shaded area across the view shows where cold air will pool on a radiation frost night. Except for the top of the hillock in the valley centre all the lower land will be inundated by frosty air. The slopes beyond offer good sites with a three-way fall and should be good fruit-planting land.

drainage. Also since sea temperature in Spring is well above freezing-point it affords very rapid spread of cold air. There have been cases where land really close to the sea was spared the frost damage which higher land behind it suffered. This is explained by the ability of the cold air draining away to sea-level to spread out rapidly and so never retain depth near the sea.

In applying the differentiation of donor recipient a hill-top, a ridge or a small plateau are frost-proof in Spring frosts because they cannot hold up or receive air chilled by the radiation-loss of vegetation near soil-level. The continuous falling away of cold air as it develops enough weight through density to gain motion does not allow freezing-point to be reached save in conditions of frost of extreme severity. Even such tender subjects as potatoes will not be affected in moderately severe frost although on the lower levels where the accumulating drained air deepens as it travels, or begins to sort itself out into icy rivers, damage will begin and will culminate in complete disaster where the cold air pools or deepens in its flow.

Of all aspects, the safest in frost is the sizeable, solitary hill standing in the wide open plain. Where the Cotswolds face on to the vale of Evesham and towards the Malvern Hills there are several such frost-proof hills. The summits of these provide four-way drainage of cold air and suffer not at all even in major frosts. Among possible sites for fruit-growing, land with four-way drainage is seldom suitable owing to exposure to wind and drying out. Land with three-way drainage can often be chosen since that merely demands land with a fall in one direction and a tilt in two others (Fig. 6). Such land is safe provided that it is not so low as to be subject to inundation frost pooling in a valley which may rise to 150 feet depth or more. One must be sure that the site is on a donor area (see Plate 17).

CHAPTER IX

CLASSIFICATION OF FROSTY AREAS

THE following formula may be found useful in selecting or valuing sites for fruit farms in relation to their liability to frost-damage.

1. The site should have a good fall, but should not be too steep for easy cultivation or liable to erosion or drying out.

2. It is preferable that the site chosen has the minimum of higher land above, or is insulated by its contours from the main stream of air drainage from higher land.

3. Such fall as the land may have should offer two- or preferably three-way drainage. That is, a South slope should have in addition a tilt to East and West.

4. There must be an ample area of land at a lower level below the site to accommodate all the chilled air which is liable to be discharged on to it from the neighbourhood as well as from the proposed fruit-farm site.

5. Care must be taken to estimate how deeply the area below the site is liable to be inundated by feeds of chilled air from surrounding areas which may not be obvious. Several miles are soon travelled by chilled-air drainage on a long night.

6. You may regard ten feet of chilled, damaging air as the maximum build-up liable to be met with in England on level ground in the worst frosts of late April and May. Base your calculations of donor and recipient areas on this figure to be on the safe side.

7. Remember that you may do much for an orchard by noting the natural air-drainage channels as offered by the contours of your land and by respecting such channels by either using them as roads or leaving them unplanted.

8 Where a young orchard shows any liability to frost-damage this liability is bound to increase with every year's growth. Though an established orchard may be worth heating, no site which obviously needs orchard heating is worth planting up. Long weed and grass in an orchard in May will hold up air drainage to the mean height of the grass-tops.

Under the heading of The Frost Formula we have divided land contours up into three categories: donor, intermediate and recipient areas. All these areas are productive of chilled air on a radiation frost night and we will examine them separately.

Donor Areas

All high ground, plateaux and the upper slopes of hill-sides which are either the highest land in their neighbourhood or receive no cold-air drainage from outside, and which are out of the rising level of pooled cold air, must be considered as donor areas proper.

Such sites may vary from a mountain or the 1,000 foot hill to one but a few score feet above the general level of the open plain. You may, for example, compare the huge bulk of Bredon Hill, an offshoot of the Cotswolds in the wide vale of the West Midlands, with one of several small hillocks which rise from the vale of Evesham. Both are donor areas and both will show temperatures very similar to each other despite the disparity in size.

In the wide levels of Cambridgeshire any small rise is a donor area[1] because, despite its humble aspiration to Heaven, it is not overtopped by any nearby higher land. A true donor area is incapable of generating a damaging depth of cold air : this, to some extent, limits the possible area of land in this category by postulating a shape or contour, but in any case the gradation of donor area to intermediate area may be gradual and not sudden.

In the broken country around Ross-on-Wye, in Herefordshire, where very high land encloses the valley of the Wye, donor areas predominate over recipient areas, and with the outlet for all the pooled cold air limited to the steep and narrow passage of Symond's Yat a tremendous pool of chilled air forms early in the night of frost, collecting to a great depth and producing on occasion the surprisingly low temperatures for which Ross-on-Wye is famous.[2]

In this instance, though the valley area seems large, the high land is greatly in excess, and one is reminded of the story of the Scotchman and the Englishman arguing about the respective beauties and virtues of their own countries. At last the Englishman, tired of being out-boasted by the Scot, retorted, " Well, at any rate you will admit that England is bigger than Scotland ? "

[1] A district report from Cambridgeshire in *The Grower* of May 12th, 1945, states : " There are more than 5,000 acres of top fruit in this country, and not more than 300 acres in the whole county are likely to yield a medium or good crop. . . . Only a few orchards in the hills, which amount to not more than 7 per cent of the fruit acreage, have been unaffected."

[2] On February 14th, 1929, the temperature here fell to − 1° F., killing many varieties of evergreen trees.

"Na, na, mon," said the Scot. "Gin ye roll out the mountains flat, Scotland will hae twice the area."

So it will be appreciated that just as we were able to duplicate temperature records in big scale recording (see Graph 1 on p. 33) at Blackmoor with small scale recording at Leckford so we may expect similar performances in any area if we care to record frost effects, variation in degree being related to the contours rather than the size of the areas concerned.

The degree of frost reached on any given radiation frost night will be determined (a) by the size of the donor area, (b) the size of the recipient area and the depth on that area which can be reached by the pooling of cold air. The more swiftly this area fills up the longer the frost; the deeper the collected cold air the more rapid and intense the radiation loss of every exposed surface beneath it and the more devastating the frost damage in its lower levels.

Intermediate Areas

These are, in a sense, donor areas also, since they discharge their quota of cold air on down towards the ultimate levels of collection, but they must also accommodate and pass on the slightly less cold air which is coming down to them from the true donor areas.

If we therefore regard intermediate areas as generally having less fall than the donor areas it will be realised that, having a considerable feed of their own cold air to handle, plus the less cold air from the land above, the tendency of air drainage at the intermediate levels will be to lose speed, to deepen and collect before it can move on.

On land which is fairly level and gently sloping one would expect such cold-air feeds to move to lowest levels as a slow but steady flow. We have already suggested that the maximum build-up of damaging cold air during a whole night of frost should never exceed ten feet in depth on level land. Such a build-up can only occur where air is completely stagnant and where radiation loss is intense. It is unlikely, therefore, that donor and intermediate areas together provide a flow which will exceed that output during the same period and the chilled air of a seven-hour frost would pass as a very shallow stream which would amount to no more than a few inches in depth.

Unfortunately, completely level surfaces are seldom met with in intermediate areas. Trees, houses, hedges are all obstacles, and

Shelter belt trees cut up to allow air drainage.

10

This Sussex orchard did not pick one single apple in 1943. Bad
air drainage and lack of pest control saw to that.

11

Photographed for the author by
Long Ashton Research Station

The pears at top are typical specimens of Dr. Jules Guyot resulting from second blossom after the 1935 frost. Note the " bull-necked " stalk end and the curious, raised, hair-like lines running from eye to stalk.
The lower pears are specimens of Doyenne Georges Boucher. Being wall grown radiation loss was intense on the exposed side. As a result the pips on that side failed to grow resulting in one-sided development and bringing stalk and eye on to the same side. Pip development on the lower side was complete and pulp grew away normally. Just under natural size.

---

where the fall of the ground is slight and air drainage is correspondingly slow, the tendency is for the flow of cold air to back up to the height of the obstacle if the obstacle be a large one and having achieved that height to flow on over it in exactly the same way that Dr. Schmidt described the outlet of cold air from his Austrian frost-hole (see p. 17).

Every hedgerow on an intermediate area which is not roughly parallel to the line of fall is a potential barrier against drainage flow, and a hedge across the line of fall where the slope is slight must back up cold air to its own height and cause damage to any susceptible fruit planted behind it (see Fig. 4, page. 24). Where, as occasionally happens, a railway embankment skirts the lower slopes of a hill-side, cold air will back up the slope to the level of the rails, leaving behind it clear indications of its presence.

I have at times following a severe frost seen the foliage of young ash trees growing on a railway embankment blackened by frost to exactly the embankment level, leaving green undamaged leaf above (Fig. 7). On the same embankment where a road ran beneath a bridge the line of damage ceased to be level and eased down to below the level of the bridge opening, showing that the velocity of the flow of cold air through the opening had lowered the level of the pooled cold air on each side of that opening. In fact the cold air must have poured through that opening as a steady stream during the coldest part of the night and early morning.

One might imagine from such instances that the intermediate areas are as dangerous for fruit planting as are the recipient or frost-hole sites. It is quite certain that great care must be taken in choosing a fruit site in such an area. In many cases the contours of the intermediate areas will suggest that quite considerable and

---

Frost damage where fruit was already set, following the frost of May 16–17, 1935. The varieties are James Grieve top. Cox on left and Lanes Prince Albert. The circumferential ring is typical late frost damage, failure to develop with early fall being usual where frost coincides with blossoming. Bramley shows a rough corky area around the eye when moderately frosted. Just under natural size.

deep flows of draining air will develop in definite lines and will follow folds in the ground to certain obvious falls.

A substantial air-drainage current will have a tendency to draw away or reduce the depth of the cold air build-up in its immediate neighbourhood. It is for this reason that when planting fruit in an area which is in the intermediate class particular care should be taken to respect obvious natural channels which will conduct air-drainage flows. By leaving these unplanted the whole orchard area will be drained of cold air, while if planted up the whole orchard

FIG. 7.—Showing how cold air pooling against an embankment may escape.

area will be saturated to capacity as soon as the trees have grown dense enough to impede the flow.

I came across a pretty instance of this near Harrietsham, in Kent. A fruitgrower high up on steep land had a narrow grass land valley, topped on each side by woods, its outlet being under a hundred yards across with orchards planted directly below the outlet. Through this gulley the whole of the air drainage from several hundred acres of grass and arable land much higher up had to pass. I told him it seemed to me a very likely place to look for low-temperature readings on a frosty night. He replied that in 1941 the whole of the fruit in line with that gulley was cut off to a dead level of about six feet from the ground. This showed that the expected had happened and a stream of cold air had been focussed by the land contours on to his orchard (see photo, Plate 17). Only the steepness of the slope had saved the whole of his trees from damage. If he had respected that channel and had omitted the planting of about four rows of trees in the direct line of fall, all the cold air coming down from the land above would have been easily accommodated and no fruit damage would have occurred at all.

This is an example of large-scale drainage effects; now let us take a very minor one indeed. A friend whose orchard is most unfortunately sited and is invariably frosted in any major frost asked me, following the 1938 frost, to look over some high land near Midhurst Sanatorium. This land was admirably sited, and complied with every provision of the Frost Formula. It was situated at about the 400- to 500-foot level and only in one field where land contours were pronounced was there likely to be any possibility of a concentrated cold-air flow. Where that drainage line had outlet to a sunken road we duly found a few frosted oak shoots in the hedge and these were the only signs of any frost damage to be found in the whole area which was inspected.

On the intermediate areas during a radiation frost we may therefore visualise wide and narrow, deep and shallow streams of cold air following those lines of flow which land contours provide. These streams will vary in temperature according to the distance they have travelled, their depth and their speed of flow. The deeper and slower the flow the lower its ground-level temperature.

A line of flow once established will persist, but in minor frosts where the difference between surface temperature and air a little above surface is pronounced a number of comparatively fast-moving, shallow flows may operate, while in a major frost these will merge into a few considerable streams of cold air.

The uneven damage to young oak foliage will have been noticed by many people and is attributable to these flows,[1] but that aspect will have to be dealt with under Direct and Indirect Radiation Loss in Chapter XI. Having explored the Intermediate Areas we

---

[1] There are among oaks as among beech and other trees individual specimens which are always ahead or behind their neighbours in coming into leaf. This complicates matters a little in frosts of moderate intensity, since degree of damage and state of development would seem to be correlated.

will now move on to the Recipient Areas or frost-holes proper.

Frost-holes

A frost-hole is simply a formation of land which allows the primary accumulation of cold-air drainage and the ultimate build-up of low temperature air. It may be natural, as in a saucer-shaped depression or a closed valley, or it may be caused by the planting up of trees across a very gentle slope or in a valley bottom which, but for the presence of these trees, would have fall enough and outlet enough to pass the chilled air.

A frost-hole may be yards across or it may be spread over a hundred or more square miles as is the case of the Kentish weald. Frost-holes are just as prevalent on high ground as on low and anyone who drives along the road between Stanway and Stow-in-the-Wold in the high Cotswold country on a frosty Spring morning may pass through a dozen or more dips, where every blade of grass and every hawthorn bush is white with hoar-frost, while every rise shows the bushes clear of any suspicion of rime.

As a rule, however, the low levels are the ones which suffer, valley bottoms being particularly afflicted. You will find a few instances quoted in this Chapter, under the Frost Formula.

From the donor areas then we have cooled air passing on to join up with the flows from the Intermediate areas. This cooled air will continue its travels as the upper layer of the main drainage feeds to the recipient areas in company with the colder air generated on the intermediate levels. Once there a condition of equilibrium or stagnation will develop and the cooled air draining from the high land will be lifted up hour after hour by the steady influx of drainage air from the intermediate areas plus the rise in depth of much colder air generated at the bottom of the pond or lake of coldest air.

The coldest air will of course lie always at the bottom, and since all surfaces at the bottom of this pooled cold air are deprived of any substantial difference in air temperature radiation loss there is rapid and severe. (See Fig. 5, p. 29).

It has been suggested by some authorities that the drainage movement of cold air from hill-sides down to its ultimate level is "turbulent." With all due respect and because one can actually trace the movement of air flows by most critical damage to susceptible foliage and because on a hundred square miles of frosted territory one can see the line of frost damage as level as though it were a tide mark, I beg to disagree. Under conditions of no wind these flows are almost as level as would be the case with water. Possibly some observations on the frost of May 16th/17th, 1935, would be helpful in proving this.

Plate 8 shows a bird's-eye view of a fruit farm which I was managing in 1935 when the great frost of May 16th/17th occurred. The figures on the left-hand side of the picture indicate feet above sea-level, and damage was recorded exactly where land contours determined at all heights from approximately 800 feet above sea-level to 300 feet.

Field No. 1, planted to apples and pears, and with Morello cherries planted in a wood clearing at the lower end of the field, showed damage where the high shelter belt allowed cold air to accumulate. Damage is indicated by black, while the arrows show the direction of main cold-air flows.

Field No. 2—Apples : Only in the slight dip between the shelter belts has damage occurred. This is due to the land above draining cold air on to this section and the concentration of that air into a natural channel. Note how between Fields 2 and 3 the main bulk of cold air from the upper slopes of the hill was forced into the narrow channel between the bank of apples in No. 2 and a steep grass bank planted to plums in Field 3. All these plums were frosted black to a rigid line which showed the exact depth of the cold-air flow.

Fields No. 4 and 5—Here again cold air from above was shepherded down by a stone wall and the shelter belt running parallel with the line of fall of the hill-side. At the bottom of these fields it met an obstruction, in the shape of farm buildings, most of the stream being diverted to a grass field and a small proportion backing up behind walls at the foot of the fields.

Field No. 6—Apples : Cold air accumulated in the only level section of the field which is closely planted and spread into Field 5, ultimately draining over into the bottom of Field 7.

Fields No. 7 and 8—The left-hand side of number 7 was planted to Morello cherries, the right hand to apples. Both escaped all damage save at the extreme bottom corner where the dark patch shows an area of pooling. This field has the ideal three-way fall and no cherry fruitlet was damaged.

Field No. 8—Planted to apples, also held a few bush peach trees which carried some fruit. Between Field 8 and the house a clipped beech hedge on the field side of the road was frosted to a height of just over four feet from the road-level showing that the sunk road was carrying a full bore of air.

Field No. 9—This was the most interesting field of all, for, though the lowest, it escaped all damage save for a small patch in the extreme north-west corner where a few Victoria plums showed the mark of its passing. Other trees of this highly susceptible variety in the lower parts of the field were quite undamaged.

The line of damage to the top corner suggested that the direction of the air flow had been diverted from its original direction as determined by the land contours and had been pushed over behind the hedge on one side of a lower road. A considerable air flow coming down from above was deflected by the building at the foot of Field 5, had crossed the field of grass and found a steep descent all ready for it. Meeting the air flow from between Fields 2 and 3, it had forced that flow well off its course. Lower down this cold air completely demolished the crop in a neighbour's orchard and he was not in the least comforted by hearing that he was helping to prove an invisible hypothesis.

In all these cases of damage the persistence of the cold-air flow (which was probably not in itself at a damaging temperature) had allowed radiation loss to operate at greater intensity than was the case outside the flow where the temperature was a few degrees higher. Thus a local variation of a few degrees can make all the difference between safety and damage on a radiation frost night.

From the examination of various sites which I have been familiar with over a period of years I have found that these have behaved in 1945 as they behaved in other years. Added, however, to the radiation frost damage is the wind-borne frost damage. This has varied from sheer gale damage to the familiar symptoms of radiation-frost damage. In the latter case fruit trees on high land have, where shelter was not available, responded in the same way that susceptible varieties of tree might be expected to. Immersion for a prolonged period in wind below freezing-point has encouraged fruitlets to fall to still lower temperatures in exactly the same way that air-drainage currents on a radiation frost night will (see Chapter XI).

CHAPTER X

SOME FROSTY AND FROST-FREE SITES

MANY fruit farms examined after the 1935-38-41-44 frosts, which complied with the Frost Formula, suffered little or no damage, and it is from such land that the bulk of the fruit crop must come in bad frosty years.

On one such site after the frosts of May 1944 (and again in 1945 in the April frosts), the manager and I searched for some hours to find one single blossom or fruitlet on apples, pears and plums which had been damaged. We were unable to find even one, and the heaviest crop harvested up to date in all fruits was picked. Mr. Crane, of the John Innes Institution, who visited the fruit on 27 September, noticed one Cox in a section of cordons carrying the faintest trace of russet at the eye end. This was the nearest approach to damage he could find. The fruit farm referred to is on the Blackmoor Estate, and its temperature record is indicated by the graph on page 33.

If we examine a few typical examples we may see the application of the formula. A considerable fruit farm in the Ross-on-Wye area, sound enough in its aspect and fall and generally complying with Nos. 1, 2, 3, and 4 of the formula, suffered severe damage in its lower sections because, although donor areas themselves at the beginning of the frost, as the night wore on they became submerged in the rising level of pooled valley air which rises to more than 100 feet in depth. Nos. 5 and 6 of the formula had been ignored, since an enormous donor area drained into the valley which had a very restricted outlet. On this farm also damage occurred above the valley frost-level, where a heavy feed of cold air from some thousands of acres was concentrated into a wide gulley of considerable depth. In this gully many older trees had been allowed to grow to a great height, undergrowth had not been dealt with, and the result was that easy passage being denied to the cold air it built up to tree-top level and backed up the sides of the gulley. No. 7 on the formula had been neglected. In this case the grower decided to grub all the trees save a few good specimens and to get rid of the undergrowth. Recordings kept in the Spring following showed that the gulley was then carrying a definite flow and was no longer backing up. Frost damage here in 1945 was extremely severe, only a small percentage of a large acreage escaping.

A farm in the West Midlands, in which I had a share during and after the last War, was consistently frost-proof in most damaging frost years and has remained so ever since, giving regular and excellent crops of early potatoes and producing heavy yields of apples for its acreage even in the worst years. Of no great height above the level it consists of a slightly curved plateau of under 100 acres, falling on the North side steeply towards the Malverns and on the South and West towards May Hill and Newent. Only on the lowest levels of the last-named slope, which is within the valley pooling area, does frost damage occur. The upper section of the farm complies fully with all the desirable items of the formula.

A small orchard of a few acres between this farm and the foothills of the last of the Malverns very rarely escaped frost in any season, being a natural frost-hole. The only heavy crops ever picked there were in such glut seasons as 1921, 1934 and 1936. This orchard complied with no single item of the formula, but carried surprising crops in frost-free years.

An Essex farm of considerable acreage is bisected by a valley, the fruit having been planted up both sides and along the bottom. This fruit farm is an enormously productive one and to save the bottom fruit from frost damage literally thousands of pounds have been spent on orchard heating during the pre-war years. Parts of this farm, which comply with items 1 to 5 of the formula, normally escape frost damage, the bottom of the valley, however, since it has to pass not only the cold air draining down the valley sides (a negligible amount considering the fall) but the whole of the cold air draining from over 700 acres of land higher up which is mainly grass fails lamentably to comply with items 2, 3 and 4.

It has been mentioned that our leading research stations are not well situated against frost. If we consider Long Ashton Research Station, situated a few miles out of Bristol, we have land set in a valley with a slow fall to the open land towards Bristol itself. On either side of the valley in which the main plantations lie are hills, those on the North side being steep and rising to 400 feet and over. The South side is flanked by a small hill which is planted up, and away to the South-west and West lie big acreages of grass and arable land with a decided tilt towards the Research Station.

Royal Sovereign Strawberry Plant (*right*) buds and blossoms black-eyed after frosts May 7-11, 1944.

Sir Joseph Paxton Strawberry Plant (*left*) under 5 per cent. of blossom blackened. Both pictures taken May 20, 1944.

Norfolk Giant Raspberry (*right*) still in tight bud a month after the May frosts of 1944.

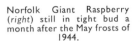

Photos: Shell Film Unit

Damage to Walnut (*left*) May 7-11. Photographed June 11, 1944, showing new shoot coming out at base.

12

Cox's Orange Pippins cropping freely 4 ft. higher up than the tree illustrated below.

Cox's Orange Pippins on the valley bottom badly frosted, 1944. See Fig. I for the explanation.

Bisecting the station from almost East and West is the railway (G.W.R.) running in a deep and wide cutting.

In minor frost years the land on the North side of the station will escape damage and in the frosty year of 1941 a very heavy crop of black currants was picked on this section. The land complies with items 1, 4 and 5 of the formula. On the South side of the station there must on frosty nights be a continual flow of chilled air from the hills which flank it on the South-west. Though these are some distance away a very big acreage of land must develop much chilled air and discharge it towards the station. At the exact spot where the flow of cold air strikes the station land it is collected and directed by a dense and high belt of larch which tops the railway cutting. This side of the station fails therefore in items 2, 3, 5. Were it not for the feed from the South-west this section of the station orchards should be reasonably safe in frosty years except for the lay-out of existing plantations of top fruit and also of shelter belts which would always tend to back up cold air where they are set across the line of flow.

It would, in my opinion, be a simple matter to set a barrage line of heaters across the only possible point of entry of cold air to destroy this, and were that done the plantation contours should be able to look after their own chilled air and that from their immediate neighbourhood. Could the lay-out have been designed to take advantage of the wide deep railway cutting as a natural air-drainage channel of superb design most of Long Ashton's frost troubles would have moved on to Bristol and the river.

East Malling Research Station is set in a very much wider valley than Long Ashton, but is liable to increasing frost damage as its plantations grow more dense. Backed by high land on the South and facing down into the valley of the Medway, it has little height above the valley bottom. On the West, no more than five miles away, lie high hills, and on the East, towards Maidstone, lie the North Downs. The site itself has a very slow fall towards the North. It must, therefore, be classed as failing in items 1, 2, 3, 4 and 5 of the formula. Actually its situation is not as bad as this sounds since the fall of the land behind it does not direct the bulk of its cold air directly upon the station. There is also a railway on a considerable embankment running East and West directly above the station land which must cause the cold air to back up before flowing over its top and this would suggest an admirable line for a barrage of orchard-heaters. The Medway valley is wide enough to take a big flow of cold air, and only on major frost nights will frost back up from the valley below and inundate the station site.[1]

At the same time one has only to examine such spots as the mainly well sited cherry orchard at the Rocks Farm above the station to see how the crop can be wiped out in those dips which can hold up the cold drainage air. After the 1935 frost the hill-side at the top of the long slope down towards East Malling on the Malling-Wateringbury road showed in one spot exactly how much cold air a close plant could hold up. In this case a coppice of chestnut had been cut a year before and a dense level growth of young chestnut resulted. The whole of that level growth was browned to the top by frost, but above the general level where an occasional shoot had gained an extra foot or more of growth the leaf remained green. That actual coppice had filled up with cold air to capacity and the stream had then flowed on over it leaving undamaged those shoots which stood above its flowing level.

At the same time it is interesting to note that while one site may be in the drift of cold air and affected by radiation conditions in one year the other station may escape. In 1944 Long Ashton had a useful crop, while East Malling suffered fatal damage. In 1945 it seems as though conditions were reversed.

In the blizzard and wind-borne frost conditions of 1945 exposed sites in the West Midlands suffered severely. Some of the damage was caused by low temperature and some by wind buffeting. In Devon and Dorset trees were blackened or browned by frost damage. In exposed sites in Oxfordshire I saw hedges browned on the N.W. side and clear of damage behind, trees also in fully exposed positions were completely blasted, those in sheltered positions were undamaged or only the tops scorched.

Indications suggested that while much damage had been caused by radiation frosts in the low-lying orchards of East Sussex and some damage by wind, the Maidstone area, including East Malling and much of the Weald, had escaped major damage by radiation frost. Growers told me that during such nights as favoured this type of frost development they were surprised to find light

---

[1] Unfortunately when this site was planted up no allowance was made for air drainage, trees and hedges being set across the line of the fall. This, though preventing air movement, would facilitate general orchard heating, and an undertaking of such importance to the industry should be fully equipped to cope with frost. If the oil fuel firms were as enterprising as they should be, salvation by heating on a site so much visited should be first-class advertising for them, and need cost the station nothing.

cloud or haze persisting with unexpectedly high temperature readings.

As the main drift of cold wind and weather was from the north-west I should put this haze down to the effect exerted by smoke-drift from London's millions of chimneys across this particular area.

A micro-climatological note was sent me by a Herefordshire friend who on higher land had in 1945 lost most of his fruit to the effect that on a low-lying site beside a large prisoner-of-war camp the smoke-drift from the kitchens had saved a stretch of fruit from damage. This on a small scale suggests what effect may be expected on a large scale.

In the West Midlands almost under the shadow of the Malvern Hills the Perdiswell Demonstration Station is hopelessly engulfed in the pooled cold air of the plain near Worcester and fails in every item of the formula.

Finally, we have the classic example of the R.H.S. Gardens at Wisley. Here variety trials of fruits have been in progress for years, but what trials can be conclusive when trees are planted on a soil few growers would care to work and are sited in a frost-hole which must condemn the crop to failure in any frosty Spring?

The fruitgrowers in this country are immensely indebted to their research stations, a compliment which I am sure the latter would return, but if we are to grow fruit after the war is over as it could and should be grown in England, we badly need at least one research station which has a frost-free site, so that trials may be trials and not trials and errors.

CHAPTER XI

DIRECT AND INDIRECT RADIATION LOSS

IN major frost years the relative difference in temperature between air at soil-level and a few feet above can give quite different frost results. The 1935 frost, for example, was what may be described as a sticky frost since, although temperature at soil-level was very low, the general air temperature was also low, with a result that the air draining away to bottom levels moved slowly and deepened where sluggish movement favoured the development of local pooling. Every shelter belt across the line of flow, every clump of trees backed up the slow-moving rivers of cold air, and the result was that a most damaging frost in many normally frost-free places developed. The big frost of 1941 was of a faster-moving type, and damage, though severe in many places, was not nearly so consistent as in the 1935 frosts, particularly where farms lay in the area between true donor and ultimate recipient stages. The 1944 frost also moved fast, and living in a house with a garden badly frosted in 1941, I was glad to note that the removal of a hedgerow by a neighbouring farmer not only offered a strategic outlet for cold air which normally passed over my garden, but probably drew away such cold air as collected and prevented it pooling to a damaging level. These conditions and results were again repeated in 1945. Such small items as hedge-grubbing may have profound effects on local micro-climatology.

To the fruitgrower who has trees planted in a frost-hole nice discriminations of degree are of no great interest. If a Spring frost comes and he does not care to heat his orchard he must suffer the penalty of a bad site, his crop is spoiled and that is all there is to it.

Nor do such distinctions concern the grower who has his fruit on a safe or donor site. If, in spite of wise choice of position, he still suffers serious damage (a very unlikely contingency) then he can be quite sure either that his shelter belts and hedges need alteration or that the frost was of such phenomenal severity that no fruit in the country subject to that particular freeze will have escaped.

It is the grower on the intermediate areas who is faced with all sorts of apparent anomalies and contradictions. Why, for example, should some of the oak trees in his immediate neighbourhood carry branches whose foliage is blackened by frost while other branches do not seem to have suffered at all? Why should the top of his nicely-clipped box hedge be bleached white by frost while its sides remain undamaged? Why should the pears and peaches on his wall be sound and swelling visibly while a few yards away in the open his pears and plums have hardly a sound fruit left among the lot of them? Why, too, should the topmost branches of his black currant bushes have all their fruit stripped off while branches lying near the soil carry a full complement of berries? Surely the coldest air must have been near the ground-level? Then the strawberries—why should an odd cloche, open both ends, left above a plant or two, prevent blossoms from being black-eyed like the rest of the patch? These are all natural and obvious questions, and we will answer each in turn, but first we had better define Direct and Indirect Radiation Loss.

Direct Radiation Loss

Only such surfaces as are completely exposed to the sky from horizon to horizon suffer full direct radiation loss. The upper surface of a leaf facing the sky can suffer it, but a leaf lying below another leaf is shielded wholly or in part from full loss. The top of a brick wall will suffer the extreme of direct radiation loss, but the sides of the wall will not. The roof of a house will lose far more warmth by radiation than will the walls, so that we find after a radiation frost night hoar-frost on the wall-top and the roof-top, but not on the wall faces.

What this amounts to is that the horizontal surface is exposed to radiation loss through an angle of up to 180 degrees, i.e. from horizon to horizon, while the vertical surface, though it can lose heat through a possible angle of 90 degrees, must receive radiation from the surfaces which make up ground-level. The top of the wall can suffer full direct radiation loss, but the wall face cannot.

Both vertical and horizontal surfaces are exposed to indirect radiation loss because the air surrounding them is liable to be chilled to a temperature below that at which the exposed surface stands at the beginning of the frost. In the frost-hole proper, when a frosty spring night is nearing its coldest period just before dawn, every blossom, leaf and fruit in the pooling area of cold air may be submerged in air cold enough to produce fatal damage. This, too, irrespective of the fact that surfaces immersed in that icy air are themselves still losing heat rapidly and are actually responsible for producing the lowest temperatures of all which may be registered at the bottom of the frost-hole. Direct radiation loss is therefore objective. Indirect radiation loss is subjective. The former is the result of facing on to outer space; the latter comes from accepting cold from local surrounding air.

Now let us look at the instances we quoted before. If we consider the partially damaged oaks in the intermediate areas we shall find that full damage to leaf or bud occurs where the branch projects outward and is fully exposed to the sky. Interior branches may not be damaged, branches set so that other branches extend beyond them or project out at a higher level may be merely scorched at the tips or remain quite uninjured. Whole tops of some oaks will have escaped all damage.

These variations in damage are due to the fact that the tree is immersed, or partially immersed, in a flow of chilled air. The temperature of such flows will, as we have seen before, be decided by their depth and speed of travel. Some are capable of causing full damage, others may not be. The temperature of the air flow concerned with the partial damage to an oak, though low is not in itself low enough to cause damage, but, since the fully exposed leaf surfaces of certain parts of the tree are themselves losing enough heat by radiation to bring them below the temperature of the air surrounding them, a temperature level is reached which is low enough to cause full damage to the exposed parts while the shielded parts remain sound and unaffected.[1]

This type of damage occurs only during major frosts in the intermediate areas. It will be found on oak, walnut, ash and beech to name but a few susceptibles.

In the recipient or frost-hole areas the general temperature of the pooling cold air, plus direct radiation loss, spells death to all tissues which are physically incapable of resisting low temperatures. As regards the bleached top of the box hedge, a damage which was very general in the May frosts of 1944 and the undamaged sides of the hedge, the top of the hedge is exposed to radiation loss

---

[1] Temperatures taken inside ripe navel oranges in American frost trials showed that a fruit exposed to the sky fell steadily from 25° F. to below 18° F. at the end of the night, while a similar fruit sheltered by foliage remained at a temperature of within a fraction of 28° F. during the same period. Tests with partially sheltered fruits approximately halved the difference between fully exposed and fully shaded fruits.

through an angle of 180 degrees, while the side is limited to a 90-degree loss and must at the same time accept a 45-degree gift of radiation from the earth itself.

Where fruit in the open suffers one has direct radiation loss operating in addition to possible indirect loss through surrounding cold air. Damage will vary in degree according to local conditions. Stray fruits will develop close up against a branch, or the trunk, or under heavy foliage, while quite useful crops will sometimes be found where a cropping tree is close up against a much larger tree and so shielded from much loss of heat, or even where a tree is hopelessly overcrowded.

The pears and peaches on the wall, as in the case of the box hedge, are limited to a 90-degree loss and must accept the 45-degree donation from soil-level. It is this which gives a border against a wall protection decreasing in effectiveness the further one goes from the wall from a line drawn at 45 degrees from the top of the wall to soil-level. The glass canopy set along the tops of peach walls cuts out a great deal of radiation loss from the peach tree as well as providing a useful line from which to hang protective fish-netting.

Indirect radiation loss or general low air temperature (so low that damage must occur) is usually responsible for the loss of wall-grown fruit and this seldom occurs in intermediate areas save where the passage of the cold air is held up or where a heavy and concentrated flow impinges on a definite spot producing a local frost-hole within the intermediate area.

I have seen such damage occur on the wall of the lowest end of a walled garden set on a gentle slope on what one would consider a good frost-free site. The damage was simply due to the collection of chilled air from within the area of the garden itself which was a big one of several acres. The remedy in such cases is to remove a section of wall at the lowest spot and install a door which can be left open on frosty nights, or to fit an ornamental iron gate which will allow all the air drainage needed. This, of course, is micro-climatology with the accent on the micro.

Damage to crops such as black currants and gooseberries may vary in degree, but in the intermediate areas in 1944 and 1945 it was common to find where air temperatures went as low as 7 degrees below freezing that denseness of foliage, by denying direct radiation loss, counted heavily in determining weight of crop. The exposed tips of branches carrying fruit were damaged by direct radiation

loss, while branches close to the ground and fruit in the centre of
the bushes being shielded from radiation loss came through with
very little damage. This behaviour was noticeable also in plums
where heavy foliage assured good crops and poor foliage resulted
in very small yields.

The response of the strawberry beneath the shelter of the
open-ended cloche shows clearly that air temperature (up to a
certain definite point) is in itself not directly responsible for damage.
Yet that undamaging air temperature, which would be more or less
equal inside and outside the cloche, was low enough to allow fully
exposed objects to lose heat to the point where they reached a
damaging degree of cold, while the plant beneath the shelter of
the glass of the cloche was prevented from such loss by the reflection
of heat radiated back from the glass. One might say that the air
standing at a minimum during the night of 28° F. allowed fully
exposed objects to fall to 23° F. while sheltered objects still stood
steady at 28° F. or slightly above.

Direct radiation loss can vary considerably in degree. It may
develop slowly and attain little intensity or it may be speedy and
severe. The latter and most damaging type is determined by the
clearness of the atmosphere at the time of the frost. The frost
of 1944 caused severe frost marking to susceptible varieties of apple
on many fruit farms which normally escape spring frost damage
but, at the same time, some unusually heavy crops of frost-marked
apples matured.

To combat direct radiation loss the free movement of air is
essential. In a very large Bramley orchard at Lingfield scarcely
an apple matured, even in the highest part of the orchard, on the
outside of the trees without severe frost-eye though fruit was fairly
plentiful on the inside of the trees under the foliage. At Blackmoor
in Hants at the 400- to 500-foot level no single specimen bearing
this type of damage could be found in a very heavy crop. In the
first case land contours do not favour rapid air drainage while in
the latter they are entirely adequate.

Following this frost I noted the damage in well-sited orchards
in Suffolk. Normally, secure against damage in moderate frosts,
their land contours were insufficiently pronounced to ensure the
rapid falling away of chilled air to lower levels with the result that
radiation loss built up rapidly. Frost-marking and partial loss of
crops resulted.

On one farm the maintenance of a very high hawthorn hedge,

Forty-year-old Bramleys. Air can move more freely here, but the site in Surrey is not frost free. Much fruit in 1944 was "frost eyed," but a fair crop resulted.

Eighteen-year-old Cox cordons in Hampshire. A good fall and clean cultivation allows good air movement. 860 bushels of Cox and 61 bushels of pollinating varieties were picked here on one acre of ground in 1944.

14

RECIPIENT
AREA
Cultivated Black-
berries blasted by
34 frosts in April-
May, 1938, in the
valley bottom of
graph No. 2.

DONOR AREA
Cultivated Black-
berries in full
bloom at 500 ft.
up where no frost
was registered.
Both photos taken
in same week.
June 27-28, 1938.

15

invaluable in windy weather, was obviously slowing down air movement to such an extent that damage in its immediate neighbourhood was pronounced.

High hedges must always be suspect unless they run parallel with a good line of fall. If set across the line of fall wide gaps in the hedge must be provided at intervals to allow easy passage to air drainage. This applies even where the fall is good, for stagnant or semi-stagnant cold air will most certainly back up to the level of the hedge-top, and once this has happened much lower temperatures will develop within the area of pooling.

Plate 9, opposite page 33, shows a very tall and heavy shelter belt hedge running across high land at Blackmoor, with higher land above it and ample land below to take cold air. The gap in the hedge was cut two years ago and has served very well, yet the only apple on which a suspicion of frost-eye could be seen was close to the upper side of this hedge on a patch of cordon Cox which picked 860 bushels to the acre in 1944 [1] (Plate 14).

From this it will be seen that while shelter from prevailing winds is an excellent thing every effort should be made when planning fruit farms and planting fruit to so arrange the hedgerows that they do not in any way hinder air movements on frosty Spring nights. Such movements are not connected with wind but are purely relative to land fall and contours. Their course can therefore be easily and certainly plotted. If shelter must be planted across the line of fall then larch or spruce which can be stripped of their lower branches when they attain a reasonable height will allow cold air to pass through their bottoms while the tops will give useful wind shelter.

These instances should serve to show that direct radiation loss in air which is cold, but not cold enough to cause damage to susceptible tissues, can be responsible for much loss of fruit. It also suggests that much more use of cover could be made than is the case to-day. The single floorboard supported on a couple of bricks above an early row of potatoes will reduce frost damage to a minimum in many places. A pitched roof two feet wide above a row of cordon apples or choice pears will serve the same purpose and will provide a handy support for a hessian curtain to be slung if the weather is really severe at blossom time.

Always in Spring frosts one should seek to cut out the direct radiation loss. The Germans at the outbreak of war were selling

[1] A bushel is 40 lbs. 860 bushels is approximately $15\frac{1}{3}$rd tons of fruit.

E

a machine for fogging down an area with chemical fumes, but if properly sited the smoky bonfire may serve the same purpose provided that the cover can be maintained. Cold air may work its way in below the smoke, but the intensity of radiation loss will be reduced.

CHAPTER XII

INDICATIONS OF FROST DAMAGE

THE following table has been printed in various papers both in America and in Australia and is said to have proved reliable in those countries. It is difficult to see how this can be since as we know the response to frost damage is determined mainly by variety and by the condition of the blossom stage which happens to coincide with the frost. Browning of the petals is a certain sign of frost damage, and in the early stages of blooming the whole truss of apple blossom will wilt and shrivel to a dry brown mass when severely frosted.

We know that a Bramley bloom is killed at a temperature which leaves the Worcester Pearmain perfectly happy and contented. Bramley will develop a " frost-eye " on surviving fruitlets as the result of a quite moderate freeze, though the condition is general on those apples which at the time of the frost were pointing skywards and were fully exposed to full radiation loss around the eye of the fruit. It is often forgotten that while weight will bring the apple into a downward position the tendency of the great majority of the blossoms is to face upwards and outwards, so that the position of the fruit at the middle or end of the season may be quite different to its position in May.

Here is the table for what it is worth.

A. shows buds closed but showing colour.

B. shows full bloom stage.

C. shows small green fruits formed.

Variety of Fruit	A. °F.	B. °F.	C. °F.
Apples	25	28	29
Peaches	25	27	30
Cherries	28	28	30
Pears	25	28	30
Plums	25	28	30
Apricots	25	28	31
Walnuts	30	30	30

* All these temperatures relate to air temperature as recorded by screened thermometers. Orchard temperatures as recorded by unscreened thermometers may well be several degrees lower.

These are said to be the temperatures that can be endured

for thirty minutes or less provided the temperature has not been below 32° F. for more than two hours.

One wonders how these figures have been arrived at since different varieties of all our fruits vary so much in response to frost. Since the temperatures given are those recorded by screened thermometers they give little indication of the actual temperature at which flower-bud or fruitlet stood under exposure to direct radiation loss, they merely show general air temperature.

One of the most striking signs of damage in the apple, and one which persists right through the season and so is a useful indicator of frost liability, is the crinkling of the young leaf of the blossom truss and the rupture and expanding of the main veins of the leaf owing to the separation of the upper and lower leaf surfaces by the formation of ice within the leaf. This only occurs on the developing leaf at a certain critical stage and below a certain temperature probably in excess of 6° of frost. Older leaves are unaffected and un-developed leaves develop into normal leaves. Where this can be noted in an orchard in one place and not in another a frost pocket is indicated, or else a persistent current of chilled air which allows direct radiation loss to come into play.

When a severe frost has occurred it is possible to pick a fruitlet and pull away the green covering below the calyx cup. This is commonly known as " popping " an apple, and the slackness of the skin (caused no doubt by ice formation in the cambium layer with consequent expansion of the external covering) may take up again provided the internal organs of the fruitlet are not killed. This condition was common enough in 1938 and again in 1941, though in the latter year the extreme lateness of the season con-fined the damage to early varieties which had reached blossom stage.

After any serious frost in the Bramley pink-bud stage the centre blossom of the truss of this variety will be found to be discoloured internally. Pollen will be brown and the delicate style in the centre will be darkened right down into the five pip pockets of the fruitlet (Fig. 8). The pollen-bearing anthers in the less forward buds may be damaged in whole or in part without injury to the style or the ultimate set of the apple. The bold blossoms of this variety are most susceptible to frost damage and Bramley's will be bare of all fruit following a frost which has not even thinned the Cox's. Bramley is also particularly liable to show the sheath of the fruitlet ready to part company from the body of the fruitlet below the petals taking the lower side of the sepals with it.

All these conditions indicate that the internal expansion of water as it turns to ice is the agent which disrupts or forces apart those portions which contain or are supported by sap. The formation of frost-ring around the centre of a fruit, a type of damage most common where the frost is a late one and finds the fruitlets growing away from the flower stage (by May 12, 1945, frost-ring marking was clearly visible on many varieties), indicates the area which is most heavily charged with water and which being in line with the pip pockets is the approximate line from which the main expansion of the fruit takes place.

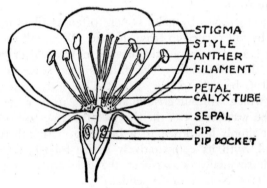

STIGMA
STYLE
ANTHER
FILAMENT

PETAL
CALYX TUBE

SEPAL

PIP
PIP POCKET

FIG. 8.—Diagram of an apple blossom showing the different parts.

Pip damage by frost in apples of some varieties (notably Lord Derby, which can set a crop with very few or even with no fertile pips but which, when the fruit is grown, are usually found to be hollow-centred and mouldy inside) does not always mean that the apples will fall.

It seems, also, that provided a fruit has set and the fruitlet has received the early stimulus to growth, a frost which kills the pips within the fruit will not necessarily prevent complete development of a medium-sized apple or pear which may be pipless or contain mouldy pips at ripening time. Generally the failure of three or more pip pockets to mature pips results in the development of a slightly flat side, since the stimulus of fully active and growing pips is removed. Poor-shaped fruits usually mean that frost damage has occurred and that fertilisation has suffered in consequence.

By American authorities it is held that when an apple fruitlet is damaged by frost, water is drawn out of the cells of which the fruitlet is made up and is frozen in the inter-cellular structure of the fruit.   More recent research suggests that in addition to the ice formation between the cells the actual protoplasm of the cell will contain minute ice crystals, thus completing the breaking-up of the tissue and the drying out of the fruitlet or flower. Much the same drying out occurs to leaves of certain trees in the occasional gales which scorch up the windward side of such trees as beech, leaving them dry and browned after the gale has subsided.   The bruising of the leaf by the wind frees the sap moisture and evaporates it, leaving the leaf in exactly the same desiccated condition as frost leaves the young beech leaf after a bad May frost.

Damage to leaves by gales is very often ascribed to scorching produced by salt carried in from the sea.   Were salt the damaging factor few sea-side trees would survive, nor would damage extend as far as the Midlands.   The fact is that some trees present a solid leaf barrier to the gale.   The leaf must then take a beating which will pulverise it and break many a stem and mid rib.   If one watches a tree in the gale the response of a beech is pitiful.   It simply lies down to a buffeting.   An ash tree, on the other hand, with its comparatively sparse foliage, sets every leaf floating horizontally and passes the gale with a minimum of damage.   (See Note 1 in Appendix.)

Where wall pears are grown (with the exception of Conference and a few others which can manage with few or no pips) a severe frost is likely to show that on the side of the fruit facing full radiation loss (i.e. the side fully exposed to the sky), growth is slowed down and while the underneath side develops normally, the exposed side having lost its pips fails to grow out and a mis-shapen fruit results (see Plate 11).   Where pears, grown in the open, are frosted—and quite severely frosted, a few varieties will survive and produce a crop of seedless fruits of regular shape as opposed to the lop-sided wall fruits.   Some varieties of pear suffer damage, but such fruits as survive are externally perfect, the worst damaged specimens having fallen as immature fruitlets.   It was common, after the 1938 and later frosts, to cut through Conference pears and find the centre black and unappetising, and though the fruit did not store so late as usual it was edible until after Christmas.

A second blossom on Dr. Jules Guyot and Laxton's Superb

pears will provide a few poor fruits, bull-necked and badly shaped as shown in Plate 11.

From all these indications it would seem that water content of the individual variety at the time of the frost decides the degree of damage suffered.[1] We know that a fruit bud in winter can withstand zero temperatures without damage, but that from the beginning of its Spring development right through until after the petals have fallen it is increasingly vulnerable to frost-damage.

Stage of development plays a big part. Whereas in the frost of May 16th/17th of 1935 the damage inflicted was mainly to fruitlets already set, the frost of May 15th/16th of 1941 coincided with a very late season and found much bloom still unopened. In the 1935 frost not only was frost-eye common in Bramley's, but Lane's Prince Albert, James Grieve, Cox and others carried a complete ring around their centres (see Plate 11).

How does frost-eye occur? If you will look carefully at a corrugated iron roof which is overhung, and so sheltered, by a tree you will notice that quite early after sunset on a radiation night moisture has condensed on the roof except where it is shaded. This is because radiation loss has brought the local temperature of the corrugated iron down to dew-point and below causing moisture to condense upon it. If you examine the sheltered part of the roof you will find it still dry because it still retains enough of the day's heat to keep it above dew-point and so dry. I think that this condition can be duplicated in miniature where bud-tips, or even blooms, are exposed to the night sky. So many of the frost markings on certain varieties of apple in 1944 are obviously related to the shading or lack of it provided by the sepals (for explanation of flower parts see Fig. 8). In that year I counted hundreds of Cox's with five-starred markings as in Fig. 9.

As with the exposed roof so with the exposed tip of the bud or fruitlet. Moisture condenses from the air on to the skin of the apple at the critical dew-point temperature. It condenses first where the sepals fail to shade the skin and frost forms there, damaging the skin in those sections, the five sepals splitting what otherwise would be a frost-eye into five sections.

So critical is this damage that great variation in effect will be

---

[1] Confirmation of this is afforded by the following illustration. From a row of runner beans, closely planted to allow further removal of alternate plants, the removed plants showed no damage from a frost which killed the original well-established row. The moved plants had lost water and were unable to accept a normal intake, a fact which saved their lives.

visible. Bramley's Seedling almost invariably gets a full frost-eye after petal-fall. It seems likely that frost-eye is a blossom-time or pre-blossom damage. Later post-blossom damage suggests that freezing takes place where the growth, and so moisture content, is concentrated. Growth being most active around the centre of the fruitlet when set is confirmed, a ring is formed as shown in Plate 11. On May 12th, 1945, frost ring markings were clearly visible on Miller's seedling apples. Ten days after the last severe frost curious worm-like markings developed on this apple.

Very unusual frost markings on pears followed this blizzard frost. Many varieties showed patchy russeting foreign to their normal complexions. The variety William's showed large russet

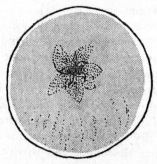

Fig. 9—Frost-eye on Cox's Orange Pippin, the shape of which is clearly related to the position of the sepals at the time of the frost.

patches and pits. On Laxton's Superb, which has William's parentage, the russet patches and pits were even more pronounced, and deep radial grooves developed from near the eye down towards the stalk. I think that these russeted markings were caused by sleet or snow congealing and freezing in patches on the skin during that wind-borne frost, with the result that moisture was drawn out of the skin directly beneath the freezing sleet. The radial grooves are not easily explained, but would seem to be in some way connected with the make-up of the fruit in relation to the position of the internal core lines.

There are, therefore, two periods of possible damage to the apple which may permit survival and normal development except for disfigurement. In addition, however, to frost-eye and frost-ring, there is the problem of " cracked russet."

Looking down into the Kentish Weald from above Boughton Monchelsea, a safe site with a good fall to lower levels.

16

A frosty bottom in Devon, looking towards Dartmoor.

The line indicates the inundation level of a valley at about 450 ft. with land running up over 700 ft. on both sides. It is about a mile due north of Aldbourne in Berkshire, S.W. of the old Roman Road between Newbury and Cricklade.

Very shallow damage to beech due to an air current directed from point immediately above the centre of the field gate and running down into the valley of the Windrush at Upper Swell near Stow in the Wold. Very critical damage can always be traced in this area.

17

In the past twenty years large plantings of Cox's Orange Pippins (see Plate 19) have been made, and now that they are into fruit a trouble peculiar to this apple is becoming accentuated. Known as " cracked russet," it can take heavy toll in frosty seasons.

The description applies to the coloured cheek of the apple, which, following surface russeting early in the season, cracks before full development is reached and finishes as a cull in the pack house, if it has not already rotted on the tree or the ground below the tree. Some slight surface russeting is normal to several dry-skinned varieties, while the greasy skinned sorts never russet except for those distinctive markings produced by severe frost or by copper-lime dusting.

All sorts of causes have been suggested for this trouble—spray damage resulting from sprays themselves, or from cold winds following, stock influence, soil drought and location of orchard and condition of the tree—but none of these suggested any single factor to which cracked russet could be related, though all might be regarded as contributory.

It may be noticed that in the latest edition of *Fundamentals of Fruit Growing* (American) the authors describe Cox (quite falsely) as a " half-russet variety as grown in England . . . a smooth-skinned fruit as grown in the Okanagan region of British Columbia." They ascribe the russet to the damper climate of our country. Since Essex, with as low a rainfall and humidity as any country in the kingdom, suffers as much from cracked russet as anywhere else, while producing perfectly clear-skinned Cox in abundance, as also does the much wetter West, the suggestion of a damp climate as productive of russet does not seem very helpful.

Spray damage may assist in producing the trouble, but, since unsprayed trees suffer just as much as well-sprayed ones, it is not a prime factor in the argument, nor does the presence or absence of cold winds around spraying time point a clear moral.

As for stock influence, it is a regrettable fact that Cox on Type IX will crack badly, irrespective of russet being present, when heavy rain follows a long drought, this cracking being mainly around the base of the apple. This particular cracking is seldom, if ever, found on well-grown healthy trees on crab stock, with a bigger rooting system, and must be regarded as a functional and seasonal disorder rather than a varietal trouble, and should not be confounded with cracked russet.

It has been suggested by one well-known Essex grower that

the trouble begins in the green-bud stage of the blossom, and, while personally I think that this is a little on the early side, the buds not being fully separated at this stage, I suggest that it may be as early as pink-bud or long after petal-fall, and that the damage is caused by excessive cooling of the exposed side of the bud or fruitlet by direct radiation loss on clear, cold nights.

The apples shown in the illustration, reading from the left to the right, are Cox, Grieve and Lane's Prince Albert. They are scarred fruits which survived the blossom-time frost of May 16th/17th, 1935, and are interesting as showing how the temperamental Cox russeted and cracked on the cheek only as compared with the " all-round " response of the other two. Note that this damage to Cox, which is merely an aggravated form of cracked russet, developed from the blossom stage and not as a summer trouble (Plate 11).

In 1944, also a frost year, and one which produced one of the heaviest crops of " frost-eyed " fruit I ever remember—whole trees of such apples as Bramley (Plate 21) and Blenheim Orange, carrying little else but frost-marked fruit—cracked russet on Cox was only prevalent in such places as were most liable to frost damage. In this year, also, Cox carried the frost-eye even where cracked russet was not in evidence.

If the theory of early damage is correct the liability of any individual fruit to damage by cracked russet would seem to be a critical pre-blossom damage with a possibility of frost-eye as a blossom-time blemish. Damage may well be decided firstly by the aspect of the blossom cluster and secondly by the position of the fruitlet in that cluster. Position is not the only limiting factor, since not all flowers set, and not all set fruits pass the June drop, and mature. A perfect fruit is far more likely to develop than a damaged fruit, and the set is unlikely to exceed one to ten, save in very exceptional circumstances.

Cracked russet will usually be found among the most exposed, highly-coloured apples or where the foliage is poor. You are less likely to find it near the ground or where the fruit is well-shaded and green. Fruit which does not colour, owing to its position on the tree, does not suffer. On that basis one might infer that exposure to light was the cause, but I think that exposure to darkness is far more likely, if for darkness we read " radiation loss."

Exposure to a low temperature of one side of a fruitlet may be expected to toughen the skin on that side, and reduce its ability to expand with the growth of the pulp within. As internal development proceeds the only expansion possible on the part of the skin is to crack at the toughened part, with the result that we describe as " cracked russet."

Growers should see how far they can relate this theory to their own crops, bearing in mind that a dozen factors may be contributory to this particular damage.

Apples and pears having a number of pips are better off than the cherry with its single stone and consequently its single chance of survival. The danger point as regards frost seems to show considerable variation as regards variety and locality, and especially is this the case when the bud is still closed but colour showing. Once blossoming is passed a drop of 4 degrees below freezing may do a deal of damage, but in estimating what temperature is experienced by a tall cherry tree a thermometer set at four feet above the ground is not of much use.

Even in a frost-hole proper where pooled cold air collects and rises to 100 feet or more in depth the coldest layers are near the ground. The air in the region of the 100-foot mark is the air cooled in the earliest stages of the development of the frost continually lifted to allow room for the ever colder air developing or coming in. Because of this it is common to find some fruit at the tops of tall trees, though all may have been frosted below that level.

Plums, like cherries, have but a single chance of survival, and blossoming as they do so much earlier than apples it is usual in a May frost to find the fruitlets blackened on the outside. There is great variation in the resistance of plum varieties to frost, and while sap content is again probably concerned there is no doubt that the protection by leaf or the lack of it at the time of the frost has a good deal to do with their survival or destruction. Victoria and Merryweather are both ill provided with leaf at blossoming time and are thus liable to direct radiation loss in a much greater degree than are the Yellow Egg Plum, Prolific, Giant Prune and Warwickshire Drooper, which are all frost-resistant types. Czar seems to be inherently resistant. The Myrobolan, or Cherry Plum, being the first to come into bloom gives sure indication of the frost freedom of any site where it is able to set its fruit after an inclement Spring. Cherries after frost will show a dull olive tint on the exposed fruits and any interior discoloration of the stone indicates fatal damage.

CHAPTER XIII

VARIETAL SUSCEPTIBILITY

FRUITGROWERS have long recognised the fact that varieties of apple and pear show wide variation in susceptibility to frost damage. Some of the resistant types seem to be inherently resistant, others owe their comparative freedom from damage to the lateness of their flowering period. Of the former Worcester Pearmain, Laxton's Superb, Ellison's Orange and James Grieve are outstanding examples, while Newton Wonder, Royal Jubilee, Crawley Beauty and Court Pendu Plat flower so late in most seasons that they seldom become badly involved with radiation frosts. Court Pendu Plat, a small apple of the Blenheim Orange type, is so well able to come through a frosty season that in the West Midlands, where it is still favoured in farm orchards, it is always known as the " poor man's apple " or the " wise apple."

Some of the cider varieties also are very late and Medaille d'Or will often delay its blossoming well into June.[1]

Apparently inherent resistance to frost has not yet been explained. One would not suppose that there can be any considerable difference in the make-up of the sap or internal moisture content of the fruitlet of one variety to another. There is a very obvious difference in the build of a stout, lusty Bramley blossom, which we know to be one of the most susceptible of all, and the slender stalked, light bloom of a Worcester Pearmain which often shows remarkable resistance.

Since, to create the damage, moisture has to be drawn out of the cells and frozen in the area between the cells, it looks as if a definite volume of cell moisture or size of cell may be concerned with the damage factor. If one could estimate frost susceptibility by weight per hundred blossoms, allotting Bramley with its solid heavy bloom and Worcester with its light blossoms which probably weigh less than one-third, an equivalent resistance figure, estimation of varietal frost risk for other varieties would be a simple enough matter. Things do not work out in this way unfortunately.

So much depends upon the stage of development of the bud or flower that a few days' variation in full blossom date may make all the difference in ability to stand frost. The stock upon

[1] Orchards in blossom in Normandy were remarked upon by war correspondents on D day, June 6th, 1944.

which the tree is worked, too, seems to have some effect, and Mr. J. M. S. Potter of the Royal Horticultural Society Gardens at Wisley, who is particularly well situated to observe frost damage, stated after the frosts of May 7th–11th, 1941, that trees on type XII stock were more susceptible than those on Malling types I and II.

Out of the varieties included in the R.H.S. Trials at Wisley he gave the following indications of resistance. In Group 1, those varieties which were only partially injured and carried heavy crops were—

> Crawley Beauty,[1] Ellison's Orange, Cutler Grieve, Red Coat Grieve, Ontario, Wagener, Laxton's Epicure, Woolbrook Pippin, Opalescent, Worcester Pearmain, Melba, Stonetosh, Laxton's Triumph, Laxton's Superb.

Group 2, those which were seriously injured and yielded only light crops included—

> Lord Lambourne, Edward VII,[1] Monarch, Millicent Barnes, Beauty of Bath, Maidstone Favourite, George Carpenter, Thorpe's Peach, Patricia, Taunton Cross, Gloucester Cross, King of the Pippins, Early Victoria, St. Cecilia.

Groups, those which had all their flowers more or less destroyed comprised—

> Bramley's Seedling, Newton Wonder,[1] Lane's Prince Albert, Encore, Peter Lock, A. W. Barnes, Alderman, Sowman's Seedling, Ecklinville, Woolbrook Russet, Cox's Orange, Seabrook's Red, Blenheim Orange, Cottenham Seedling, Herring's Pippin.

It is interesting to note that Bramley, Cox and Blenheim Orange come in Group 3 in Mr. Potter's list, but in my own garden, in 1944, in an intermediate area, although from six Bramley trees on Type IX I picked only two apples, from old standard trees of Blenheim I picked by far the heaviest crop they have ever yielded, while the same applied to standard Cox. Blenheims again had the best crop in 1945. From Cox cordons, comparable with the dwarf Bramleys for height, I harvested quite as many apples as the trees could carry. Both Blenheim and Cox were frost-eyed, but it was evident that the degree of frost (which was a maximum of 7 degrees

---

[1] Normally safe owing to late blossoming.

below freezing) was not enough to damage all the Cox internally. Both the Bramleys picked were hollow-cored and mouldy internally with no sound pips. From this one must deduce that, while all the varieties mentioned in Mr. Potter's Group 3 are liable to complete damage at the Wisley temperature of 19° F., or 13 degrees below freezing, they may have very varied resistance at temperatures of around 7 degrees below freezing.

He also stated that late-keeping varieties were more severely damaged than early or mid-season varieties. One fact which he noticed was that any blossoms which escaped injury were usually situated on the *underside* of the flower cluster. This position in the cluster cuts out direct radiation loss and its aspect is fully discussed under the paragraphs dealing with " cracked russet " in Chapter XII.

To sum up the frost liability or resistance of the main commercial varieties of apple one would describe the following as usually susceptible to frost damage in order of naming : Bramley's Seedling, Lane's Prince Albert, Cox's Orange Pippin and Blenheim Orange. Newton Wonder, though often escaping by flowering late, is susceptible enough when frost happens to come during its blossom period, and it has the added disadvantage of being a very biennial bearer.

James Grieve and Worcester Pearmain are very resistant to frost as are Laxton's Superb (Plate XXI) and Miller's Seedling, though the last named seems to have a very critical temperature below which damage is almost complete. Crawley Beauty relies upon its late flowering to escape damage as we have mentioned earlier, but late frosts may upset its resistance.

Pears react strongly to frost except for the few varieties which are able to grow on with no fertile pips of which Conference is the most striking example often producing long sausage-shaped fruits. A bad May frost will destroy most of the crop in all varieties which are fully exposed, but shelter from full radiation loss by nearness to big trees will help to give some crop where exposed trees lose all their fruit. In 1944 a row of Conference running towards a tall tree of William pears averaged only five pears per tree until the tree in the shade of the William pear was reached when over fifty pears set and grew on. Enthusiasts in pollination would of course say " Ah! We told you so. Cross-pollination is all that was needed." As, however, there was a fine set of fruit prior to the frost in all varieties, including other nearby pollinators such as Laxton's Superb, I am afraid that shelter must take the credit.[1] Pears seem to have suffered less in 1945 than in 1944 where not exposed to the wind. Williams and Pitmaston are cropping very heavily indeed in many places. (See Note 2 in Appendix.)

Plums have some very resistant varieties and where fruit must be grown at all cost without regard to quality then Czar and Giant Prune are almost certain croppers. Pershore Yellow Egg plum and Warwickshire Drooper are able to weather quite severe frosts, the latter being particularly well endowed with protective leaf and with a drooping habit which provides additional shelter. The gages seem to be very liable to loss of crop by low temperatures, while that old favourite, Victoria, with its very sparse foliage at blossoming time, is predisposed to damage. The variety Black Diamond being a very early bloomer is also liable to damage early in the season. The Myrobolan, or Cherry Plum, an excellent small preserving plum which flowers as early as the end of February in some seasons, should never be planted save in frost-free situations, but, provided that it gets through its blossoming period safely, later frosts of three or four degrees do not seem to damage the cherry plum crop. This also applies to Early Laxton, and fruit may be picked from this variety when the Victoria plum crop has been ruined.

Among the cherries Mr. Norman Grubb, of East Malling Research Station, Kent, has been kind enough to give me some information as regards frost damage " under our conditions " (these we know are inclined to be frosty). He writes :

Undoubtedly the stage blossom has reached when the frost comes has much to do with the result. My own opinion is that, in a year following a

---

[1] Many growers will have noticed that Doyenne du Comice pears carry fine crops in frosty years, apparently preferring a cold Spring. Especially noticeable is this where the site is a good one and out of the frost, or the trees are well established specimens on a wall, even though the latter be in a frosty place. While pears do not suffer from frost-eye, it seems that small radial scars at the eye end occur where the space between the overlying sepals offers full exposure of this part of the eye end. The variety showing this was Laxton's Superb.

Mr. T. Neame, a notable pear grower, of Faversham, Kent, tells me that his worst frost year was 1928, when Comice was his best cropper ; Conference poor. In 1935, Comice was poor and Conference moderate, while Pitmaston Duchess and Fertility were good. In 1938 Conference was a record crop ; Comice good, Pitmaston and Fertility moderate. The late Mr. J. Amos, of East Malling Research Station, Kent, states that in 1944, Hessle, Reine de Poires, Beurré Clairgeau, Dr. Jules, and Emile d'Heyst all cropped more or less ; in previous frosty years Conference and Durondeau have been almost the only varieties to produce anything.

heavy crop, what blossom there is is apt to be more susceptible to frost injury than usual. This view is based upon observation only, I have no accurate records to support it.

Among commercial varieties of sweet cherries, Frogmore stands out as distinctly more blossom-hardy than any other here. Kent Bigarreau might perhaps be included, but it does not seem to be nearly as hardy as Frogmore. This year two little known varieties carried practically a full crop, surrounded by trees of many varieties with no fruit at all; these were Turkish Black (Syn. Tassels Wood Black, *not* Turkey Heart) and a continental variety called Red Cluster. In the last frosty year, 1941, our trees of both these varieties were too young to crop much. Of acid cherries, Kentish Red, Triaux and Griotte de Portugal are late blossoming, and may have escaped on that account, but another acid cherry, received (probably incorrectly) as " Belle de Chatenay," is still later blossoming and had much less fruit.

Among plums, we can confirm your observation as to Czar, probably the hardiest we have. Yellow Egg (Pershore), Warwick Drooper, Giant Prune and Merryweather damson all seem moderately hardy but do not escape damage so consistently as Czar. From my garden experience I can add Angelina Burdett. Blaisdon Red failed this year, but has cropped in some frosty years.

Mr. S. Roper Dixon, of Teynham, in Kent, whose family are well-known cherry-growers, writes me of their frost susceptibility as follows :

Cherries, as you know, are vulnerable for a very long period. For argument's sake we once had a cherry crop almost wiped out by an early frost which occurred on March 10th ! This frost was so severe that it damaged, and in some cases destroyed, the young wood on several of the more delicate varieties and affected the crop in the following year. We have also had cherries frozen in the last week in May.

Cherries do not all bloom at the same time, and it depends to a certain extent at what stage the frost catches any particular variety. The blossoms are at their most vulnerable stage just before and during the time they are ready to be fertilized. It follows, therefore, that any variety which happens to be in that stage when the frost occurs is liable to damage.

I have made out two lists. The first list concerns the behaviour of cherries in March and mid-April frosts and the second their behaviour in mid-April to end of May frosts.

There is always some difficulty, owing to a variety having one or more names, in making sure that fruitgrowers understand which variety one refers to, so I have added the more popular synonyms. (See p. 73).

Peaches to be regular croppers must be grown out of frosty levels. Wall-grown peaches should have advantages over bush peaches grown in the open, but provided these latter are well up out of the frost good crops can mature in such a frosty year as 1944. Consider three examples. In a research worker's garden at Leybourne, near East Malling, are several well-grown bush

Photo taken June 4, 1938, on road between Bramdean and West Meon (Petersfield to Winchester), showing oaks defoliated by frost in May at 280 ft. level.

Photo taken June 4, 1938, a few miles farther on. Oaks in full leaf at 316 ft. level out of the frost.

18

Typical fruit above the frost level. Blackmoor, Hants, 1944. Cox's Orange Pippin.

Laxton's Superb. Perfectly pollinated fruit.

19

Resistance of various Kent cherries to two frosty periods.

Resistance Points.		Variety.	Resistance March to Mid-April.	Resistance Mid-April to end May.
Early Stages.	Later Stages.			
3	2	Amber or Kentish Bigarreau .	Moderate	Good
3	3	Black Heart	Moderate	Moderate
5	5	Bradbourne Black	Not good	Not good
7	7	Circassian or Knight's Early Black	Very bad	Very bad
2	2	Early Amber or Cleveland Bigar-reau	Good	Good
5	5	Early Rivers	Not good	Not good
5	5	Elton	Not good	Not good
3	3	Emperor Francis	Moderate	Moderate
1	1	Frogmore	Very good	Very good
4	4	Gaucher	Fair	Fair
5	5	Goodnestone Black	Not good	Not good
2	2	Governor Wood	Good	Good
7	7	Malling Black Eagle or Black Eagle	Very bad	Very bad
3	4	Napoleon	Moderate	Fair
1	4	Noble or Tradescant's Heart .	Very good	Fair
5	5	Nutberry Black or Selling Black	Not good	Not good
4	4	Ohio Beauty or Ironside. . .	Fair	Fair
5	5	Roundel	Not good	Not good
6	6	Turk or Turkey Heart . . .	Bad	Bad
4	4	Victoria Black	Fair	Fair
4	3	Windsor	Fair	Moderate
5	5	Waterloo	Not good	Not good

Degree of resistance in figures: 1 = very good; 2 = good; 3 = moderate; 4 = fair; 5 = not good; 6 = bad; 7 = very bad.

peaches. In 1943, a frost-free year, they cropped enormously carrying large, fine fruits. In 1944 there were no peaches that survived the May frosts. In early May of 1945 they promised well the area having had no severe frosts. The trees are actually growing in a site which provides the contours for a cold-air flow during radiation frost nights and in 1944 year the flow was very cold and sustained. Above East Malling, on the high land facing towards Wateringbury, the peach trees on the mile or more of walls at Barham Court were loaded to capacity—thinned out to about one per square foot of wall. The same conditions apply in 1945. All these trees were well up out of the frost. Above the

F

village of Kemerton in Worcestershire at 500 feet up some 20 bush trees of various peaches which fruited heavily in 1942 were again in 1944 carrying a very heavy crop. They have no wall to protect them, but they are growing in a corner sheltered from the South-west winds which blow hard across Bredon Hill and they are well up out of the valley frost levels.[1]

There are many sites in this country where peaches could be most profitably grown as bush trees in the open. Freedom from frost and shelter from worst winds are the two essentials for success. The fruits are much more resistant to wind than are apples. Peaches make big trees and need twenty-four feet of space in which to grow well even when worked on the Common Mussel stock, which is less vigorous than the Brompton stock usually recommended for large trees. Light rocky land will suit them better than the heavy cold soils.

Quinces are not trees which grow really well in all soils or situations. They are definitely fond of water but not of stagnant water, in which they resemble the cricket-bat willow. While growing well enough alongside a stream such a site is usually low and so more than usually liable to frost damage especially by late frosts which coincide with blossoming. If, however, a suitable site is available which is free from frost (and some upland sites combine water with a fall to lower levels), then quince should fruit regularly and be a profitable crop to grow.

Among the soft fruits the stage of development of the bud or blossom or fruitlet is often the deciding factor in degree of damage, while the amount of cover against radiation loss which the foliage gives is also an important factor. Red currants do, however, seem much more resistant to frost than black currants, but this may be because red currants are set and swelling in late April to early May when the damaging frosts are most frequent. Black currants show variation from year to year. In one season a single variety, or two out of five, may be almost a failure, while the other three fruit reasonably well. I think this is because there is considerable variation in their flowering periods, and once set some degree of immunity is conferred on the bulk of the berries, though it is noticeable that those towards the tips of the shoots or those which project beyond the cluster of the leaf, and so are

[1] In East Suffolk, at 360 feet up on cold clay land, I saw peaches of the variety Peregrine cropping heavily in 1944. The grower considers peaches hardier than plum trees.

subject to direct radiation loss, will " run " badly.   Over a period
of years in an intermediate area my best performer has been the
Hilltop strain of Baldwin, an early bloomer though late to pick,
followed by Boskoop, Davison's Eight, and with Seabrook's Black,
usually considered as a frost-resistant type, the worst performer of
the four.   This particular instance may be due to strain, but in 1944
several growers had the same experience with this popular variety.

Among the raspberries it is a foregone conclusion that the
early flowering varieties, such as Lloyd George, suffer much more
severely than the later types, such as Norfolk Giant.   In the second
week in May, in a normal season, Lloyd George has its earliest
flower trusses well exposed, and even some of the bloom out and
vulnerable.   Norfolk Giant, on the other hand, is nearly a month
later and will be in tight bud (see Plate 12).   Even in a frost like
the stinger of 1938 Lloyd George will throw out fresh flowering
shoots at the base of those which frost may have destroyed.   The
resulting crop will be late and poor, but there will be some fruit to
pick.

In strawberries the 1944 frost hit Royal Sovereign very hard
and it was noticeable that much unopened bud was blackened
within (see Plate 12).   These buds opened but failed to set
berries, as was to be expected.   In the case of Tardive de Leopold
this variety suffered badly, being also frozen in the bud and few
matured in frosty places.   Sir Joseph Paxton seems to be more
resistant than the two named, and while later than Sovereign in
coming into bloom the blooms opened clear of frost damage and
cropped well.   I find Doctor Pillnitz also very resistant.   Foliage
is a great help to the strawberry in cold seasons, and the very robust
types such as the Huxley with their mass of heavy leaf are likely
to mature more fruits than the choicer but less leafy types.

I have no information regarding gooseberries.   In my time
I have grown the commoner sorts which are resistant to mildew
and did not notice that any factor helped them to resist frost except
good heavy foliage at the time of the frost.   This is certainly a
great help to them.   Exposed specimens blister and fall with some
freedom after a frost.

Of the blackberry tribe it is probable that there is considerable
variation in frost resistance.   Himalaya Giant, robust to a degree
in growth, suffered severe damage in 1944 in my own garden.
Loganberries seem to be very resistant and these cropped more
heavily in that year than ever before, as also did the Boysenberry.

CHAPTER XIV

ESTIMATING FROST RISK AND FROST INTENSITY

HAPPY is the fruitgrower who can disregard May frosts and
sleep soundly on a starry spring night knowing that his
fruit is safe.

Some people will not believe me when I suggest that any
fruit can be safe; so the following figures, which include two
frosty years, may help to convince them. Temperature records
have been kept in this orchard over a period of years and never
once has a frosty Spring night provided a temperature low enough
to be actually damaging to blossoms or fruit, though it is likely that
the wind-frost of 1945 will have been so.

Crop in bushels (of approx. 40 lbs.) from one acre of Cox's Orange
Pippins planted as cordons in 1927.

1940	563 bushels
1941*	571 „
1942	683 „
1943	218 „
1944*	860 „ 15 tons. 7 cwts. 16 lbs.

* Frosty years.

Average crop for the last five years, 579 bushels an acre, 1941
and 1944 being frosty years. The drop in 1943 was due to hail
and bad weather early in the season. The frost of the night of
May 16th/17th, 1935, was probably the severest frost we have
experienced in 20 years. On this occasion the lowest temperature
recorded on this site was 5° F. below freezing. On the land
immediately below the temperature fell to 16° F. (sixteen degrees
of frost) with a complete wipe-out of all fruits.

This particular block of cordons is part of a fruit farm which
I know well and visit often : it is situated well up out of the frosty
levels. Its temperature graph is illustrated on page 33 and the
cordons themselves on Plate 14. With crop figures and temperature records available the reader will agree that in a case of this
sort midnight alarms and excursions are unnecessary.

Very different is the case of the orchard in a frost-hole where
heating has to be begun in time to produce and maintain heat
inversion throughout the orchard area during a long night.

To know what is likely to happen on a clear Spring night the owner of such an orchard will need a dry and a wet-bulb thermometer. The dry-bulb is simply the ordinary thermometer with an exposed, mercury-filled bulb. The wet-bulb is a similar thermometer but with a little wick which covers the bulb and dips into a water container directly beneath it. Since the wick is wet, as soon as the air tends to become dry (and the colder air is the less moisture it can hold up in suspension) evaporation will begin and this will lower the temperature of the bulb of the wet-bulb thermometer below the figure which the dry-bulb is indicating. The degree of variation of the two scales after sunset when radiation is operating will give some indication of the severity of the frost which is likely during the night and early in the morning. If the day is cold and the sky clear and the thermometer in the thirties, with the wet-bulb lower than the dry by three or four degrees *before* sunset then you can reckon on an early night frost culminating in a very severe one by morning if the sky remains clear. If the variation does not occur till some hours *after* sunset then the frost will develop in the early morning and is less likely to be severe.

If thermometer reading is too much trouble, one can buy a thermometer with a little metal contact fused into the glass tube at a pre-determined level—normally at about 3 or 4 degrees above freezing. This is connected with a dry battery and an electric alarm bell, the bell inside the owner's house, and the thermometer in the orchard. When the mercury in the tube reaches the contact the circuit is closed and an alarm bell goes on ringing until the contact is broken by hand, or the temperature rises again. Those pessimists who insist on braces *and* a belt can buy a set of ganged alarm thermometers and thus make doubly sure or even trebly sure of a warning, should frost threaten.

A barometer to keep one informed of the atmospheric pressure is a useful companion to the wet and dry-bulb thermometers, bearing in mind the fact that a radiation frost is unlikely to occur unless the barometer records a steady high pressure of the " fair " to " set fair " type.

Frost Prediction

" Long foretold, long last " is a well-known weather saw, but it hardly applies to frost which can come or go with surprising rapidity. At the critical time of the year, when fruit trees are in flower, a cold day followed by a calm and starry night is almost certain to bring a frost though not necessarily one severe enough to damage any but the very low-lying orchards.

The advent of cloud, on the other hand, at once removes the imminent threat and clouds can turn up quite unexpectedly when one lives on a small island like England with no spot more than ninety miles from the sea.

THE POINTS METHOD OF FORECASTING FROST.

First you take observations of the state of the sky and the direction of the wind. DO THIS HALF AN HOUR AFTER SUNSET.

Look then in the points scale below and add up the points as the result of your observations—points for wind direction (if strong wind add a further 8 points) and points for sky condition.

Then compare the total points with the index given here.

THE HIGHER THE TOTAL ABOVE 12, THE LESS THE RISK OF FROST.

Wind Direction Points

North-west.	5
North	4
North-east	1
East	2
South-east	7
South	9
South-west	10
West	6

Index to Scale

0–5 Frost almost certain.
6–12 Light frost probable.
13–18 Little risk of frost.
18 (and over) Frost extremely unlikely.

Wind Strength

Calm	0
Strong wind	8

Sky Conditions

Clear sky	0
Partly clouded.	5
Overcast	12

Here are three examples :

Wind N.E.	1 point	Wind N.E.	1 point	Wind S.E.	7 points
Strong Wind	8 points	Calm	0 points	Calm	0 points
Overcast	12 points	Clear sky.	0 points	Partly clouded	5 points
Total	21 points	Total	1 point	Total	12 points
Frost extremely unlikely.		Frost almost certain.		Light frost probable.	

For example, September, 1944, gave us several frosty nights which did little to help the outdoor tomato crop.[1] A warm spell followed, but the nights of October 2nd and 3rd, following brilliant,

[1] Frost about 22 September, 1943, wiped out tomatoes in frosty spots completely.

sunny days threatened keen frost at night. On the night of October 2nd in South-east England at 8 p.m. with a clear sky the thermometer at 4 feet above soil in my garden stood at 36° F. and was falling steadily. Yet when I happened to look at it at 10 p.m. clouds had come up and the mercury had risen to 41° F. But for the advent of cloud I have little doubt that freezing-point would soon have been reached.

We get these frost risks in September and October just as we get them in April and May, and the same conditions apply in each case. Opposite is a simple table for estimating the climate possibilities and probabilities which appeared in the *Daily Express*, and which the author has kindly given me leave to reprint.

This table seems to me quite simple and easy enough for anyone to understand. It gives a reasonably good general idea of frost probabilities. The conditions given in the second of the three examples approximated those of the nights of April 22nd and 23rd, 1945, when the Air Ministry suggested that severe ground frost was to be expected. It duly arrived in the low places.

The fruitgrower who heats his orchard may like further methods of estimation, so I have drawn a few paragraphs from a Pelican Book, entitled *The Weather*, again with the permission of the authors.

If, in the early evening, the sky is clear, there is no wind, the dry-bulb thermometer stands round about 40–45° F. and the wet-bulb three or four degrees lower (that is the air is pretty dry), then a ground frost is fairly certain. If, on the other hand, the air is very moist, an evening temperature of 45° F. need cause no alarm ; while with a high relative humidity and a decent breeze, even a temperature of 40° F. may not be followed by frost. Should a fog or blanket of low cloud appear later in the evening you can practically rule out the risk altogether.

Naturally conditions vary from place to place : but at Cranwell (Lincs) the following rule has been found to give the right answer more often than not. On nights suitable for radiation (less than half-clouded sky) the minimum temperature can be forecast by taking the dew-point of the air at three o'clock in the afternoon and subtracting 0° − 8° F. thus :

Mean Wind Speed expected during night.	Relative Humidity at 3 o'clock.	Formula for obtaining Minimum Temperature.
Less than 7 m.p.h.	Less than 85%	D − 8
	More than 85%	D − 6
7 to 14 m.p.h.	Less than 85%	D − 4
	More than 85%	D − 1
More than 14 m.p.h.	Less than 85%	D − 2
	More than 85%	D − 0

(D stands for dew-point at three o'clock.)

The dampness, or relative humidity, of the atmosphere may be read straight off a table once we know the wet- and dry-bulb temperatures. Roughly speaking, a difference between the two of 10° F. indicates a relative humidity of about 50 per cent. or less, according to the warmth or coolness of the day. The dew-point, i.e. the temperature at which air becomes saturated and begins to deposit its excess water vapour in the form of dew on chilled solid surfaces, can likewise be found from tables ; there is also a visual method which most of us have seen demonstrated at one time or another. To do this place an ordinary thermometer in a glass of beer, and then drop a chunk of ice into it ; when the first film of moisture forms on the outer surface of the glass, the thermometer reading will give the dew-point of the surrounding air (*verb. sap.* You needn't be alarmed—it's water, and not beer, which is running away !).

To take an example of the above method of frost forecasting : if the dew-point of the air at three o'clock p.m. is 36° F., the relative humidity 80 per cent., and a wind 10 m.p.h. is expected to blow during the night, then the minimum night temperature is given by 36° − 4° = 32° F. Try it out in the home region. If it does not work, find a set of figures for the right-hand column which do !

But perhaps you have not got a wet-bulb thermometer. In this event it might be worth while putting this American method to the test, for it requires only an ordinary dry-bulb thermometer. The method assumes (and the assumption may not be as reasonable for your particular part of the world as it is in the U.S.A.) that in typical anticyclonic spring weather with cloudy or sunny days and calm, clear nights, there is a uniform rate of fall in temperature from the afternoon maximum through the night until the early morning minimum, and that the times for such maximum and minimum temperatures will be approximately the same for all such days. This means to say that if one knows the maximum temperature and takes a reading midway between afternoon and next morning the minimum will be in ratio. Thus if the maximum temperature on any given day, say round about 3.30 p.m. G.M.T. is 70° F., and the minimum temperature is expected to occur round about 5 a.m. next morning, and the temperature at 10.15 p.m., that is midway between the times of maximum and minimum is 50° F., then the difference between the " midway " temperature and the maximum temperature (20° F. in this case) will, if subtracted from the midway temperature, give the minimum temperature likely to be recorded next morning, namely 30° F. Suppose, for the sake of argument, the afternoon maximum on the following day is only 50° F., and the midway temperature is 32° F., the subtraction of the midway reading from the maximum gives us 18° F. : 18° from 32° F. means that a drop to 14° F. is to be expected. This is an extremely severe frost and one that we can well do without.

Here, then, are three simple methods of forecasting frost with or without the assistance of instruments. If you want a simpler one still you should be able to apply to the Air Ministry, with peace here again, for a daily telegraphic forecast through the danger period. The fee for such information is quite a reasonable one.

While on the subject of forecasting, it is as well to debunk two weather beliefs. One is the reliance placed on the so-called cold periods of Alexander Buchan. Here is another extract drawn from *The Weather*.

Now, investigations of long-standing weather records show that departures from the average (whether above average or below) are often more " normal " than the average itself : indeed they occur sufficiently often in most extra-tropical lands to encourage the belief that they form a regular, even rhythmic, feature of the climate—a feature which may well be masked if we confine ourselves to arbitrary monthly or seasonal groupings of the weather elements. It was some such belief as this that sent the distinguished nineteenth-century meteorologist, Alexander Buchan, delving into the weather records of Edinburgh. What he found was very significant, although nothing like as significant as the general public has come to suppose. Among other things, Buchan noticed that between the coldest periods of the middle of January and the hottest period of July temperature showed certain well-marked fluctuations in the gradual seasonal rise and fall. After the slight expected increase towards the end of January there was frequently a marked fall about the second week in February (7th–14th) ; in the following month temperatures progressed on the whole in keeping with the march of the sun, but April (11th–14th), May (9th–14th) and June (29th–July 4th) showed frequent setbacks before the temperature peak of the year was reached in mid-July. After the expected drop towards the end of that month, early August (6th–11th) often showed a marked rise. September and October showed no conspicuous departures from the normal seasonal trend, but November (6th–13th) frequently produced one unseasonably cold spell, and December (3rd–14th) an unseasonably warm one.

Now the important point about these periods is that Buchan never claimed they were constant. On the contrary he made it clear that they were subject to variation in their incidence from year to year ; further he never claimed that they were a feature of the whole of the British Isles, but only of south-east Scotland. Actually, some parts of England do show a tendency for warm and cold spells to recur round about particular days. At Greenwich, for example, the period February 11th–14th is especially notable in this connection : in the first place February 12th is, on the average, the coldest day of the year ; secondly the five days 10th to 14th inclusive provide nearly twice as many " cold " days (10° F. or more below the annual for the year) and nearly two-and-a-half times as many " very cold " days (15° F. or more below the normal for the time of year) as the five days before or after. Early May (1st–10th) at the same station shows a little inclination to be colder than the preceding period, but the period 11th–15th (which is roughly coincident with Buchan's third cold spell) is characterised more by abnormally warm days than by abnormally cold ones. As far as warm spells go the five days August 14th–18th provide considerably more " warm " and " very warm " days at Greenwich than the five-day periods immediately before and after. Much the same is true of Buchan's last warm period : over ninety odd years December 2nd–6th has produced twice as many " warm " days (10° F. or more above the seasonal average) as the five-day period preceding it and about 50 per cent. more than that following. The most striking warm spell of all, as far as Greenwich is concerned, finds no parallel in the Edinburgh records. This is the period April 1st–5th, which is more likely to have exceptionally high temperatures (15° F. above the seasonal average) than any other five-day period of the year ; but there have been only five such days in the whole of the ninety odd recorded years ! Although some of the other warm and cold spells show greater frequencies, none of them reaches a very impressive level, either in Edinburgh or Greenwich. Even the most recurrent spell at Greenwich—February 10th–14th—only produces three " cold " days in five years and one " very cold " day every six years or so. Accordingly, the next time we are in one of Buchan's (or anybody else's) cold spells, we must not be disappointed if it belies its reputation. Even the period February 10th–14th produces one abnormally *warm* day every five years or so.

So much for Buchan's spells. There is one old saying which dies very hard and that is : " For every fog in March there's a frost in May." Again we will draw from *The Weather*.

In order to satisfy our curiosity on the point—although truth to tell, we have never seen any reason why March and May should be related in this way—we recently delved into the records of some 200 British weather stations. Two years were chosen more or less at random, and it was found in the case of the first, that for every station which showed an equal number of fogs and frosts there were two which showed more frosts than fogs (incidentally the month of May was officially described as dry, warm and sunny). In the case of the second there were *fifteen* times as many stations showing a surplus of May frosts as showed an equality of the two elements.

In the whole of the British Isles the only areas that even approached equality in the frost : fog ratio were located in the Central Lowlands of Scotland and the industrial Midlands where the fog frequency is considerably augmented by smoke pollution.

By aggregating the number of fog and frost reports for the entire country we found that in each of the two years examined there were at least *two* May frosts for every March fog ! But we are far from suggesting that this is by way of being a more reliable numerical relationship than the one above.

The Sky Thermometer

The magazine *Time*, in its issue of 3 May, 1943, under the section " Science," published an interesting photograph of a new apparatus for ascertaining the high sky temperature from ground-level. This, in some form or another, may eventually prove valuable to the meteorologist and the fruitgrower for forecasting local night weather.

The device was invented by Professor C. M. Heck, of the State College of North Carolina. So far as one can see from the photograph it consists of a nest of twelve cones rather like deep saucers, increasing in size from a small central cone about a foot wide and a few inches deep to the largest external cone about 8 feet across the rim and about 3 feet high. The cones are all made of polished aluminium sheet.

A thermometer housed in the central cone radiates its heat to the sky but is protected from the ground heat by the nest of 11 larger cones each of which is air insulated from its neighbour. When exposed to a clear night sky the thermometer in the innermost cone is thus able to cool down far below local air temperature, in fact on a radiation night it has registered a temperature as much as 47 degrees below ground temperature.

Under fog the thermometer merely records ground-level air temperature, but when clear to cloudy conditions occur each passing cloud may raise the temperature recorded by as much as 20 degrees (see Fig. 2, p. 13). Knowledge of high atmosphere temperatures and of air humidity so easily gained without having to fly balloons with instruments aboard, or send aeroplanes to the sub-stratosphere should be a great convenience in weather forecasting.

Having looked at some of the methods of frost forecasting we will now examine a few of the ways of fighting frost.

CHAPTER XV

APPROACH TO ORCHARD HEATING

IN Chapter VII we have assumed that in level country a build-up of damaging cold air (as opposed to the pooling of cold air as the result of drainage) is possible in a normal Spring frost. A build-up of ten feet is, of course, fatal to soft fruits and may cause fatal damage to all fruit, save on the tops of standard trees. Also level ground is the exception rather than the rule, and even in apparently flat country the variation in frost tide-mark following a major frost will be found to run from five to fifteen or more feet above soil-level following the lines of even slightly marked contours.

Since there is usually little or no movement of the air above level or nearly level ground during a radiation frost, orchards in these categories offer the best prospect for standard orchard heating practice, provided that this is undertaken on a fairly large scale. Small-scale orchard heating can only be operated under certain conditions which will be discussed later.

If one lights a single large bonfire in the open, if flame be present there is a tremendous upward rush of heated air or a slow upward swirl of smoke if the bonfire be a slow combustion one. The upward rise of smoke is not only caused by the fire expelling a great deal of lighter-than-air gas (for the bulk of bonfire smoke is only steam) but is because the expanded and so lighter air is under direct pressure from the surrounding cool air which forces it upward as fast as it is produced in an attempt to take its place.

A single fire then can have very little effect on the local surroundings except in its immediate neighbourhood. A great number of such fires set closely together reduces the invasion by cold air from without since a block (if one may so describe it) of air is in process of being warmed up by radiant heat from the flame and by the passage of a number of upward currents of heated air.

It is for this reason that the heating of an acreage of fruit is possible and worth while, for, when any considerable area is heated, an air circulation described as " inversion " soon begins and will continue for as long as the heat is supplied and unless a breeze springs up. Inversion or a turning back again of the warmed air rising from orchard heater pots or bonfires begins when the warmed rising air, which is cooling rapidly as it rises, reaches a temperature which coincides with that of the warmer layer of air lying well up above soil-level.

In a frost-hole of a few acres in extent which is taking and pooling the cold-air flows from a moderate acreage above it the depth of really damaging cold air may collect to a depth of no more than ten to fifteen feet. Above this cold-air layer temperature rises sharply and the inversion ceiling (i.e. the level at which cooling warm air and the upper air temperature coincide) may be no more than twenty to twenty-five feet above soil-level. In such a case a

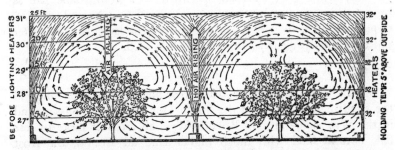

FIG. 10.—Cross-section of a row of orchard trees and orchard heaters, illustrating the manner in which temperature inversion makes effective orchard heating possible. This diagram represents air currents and temperature conditions in the orchard on a typical calm, frosty night a few minutes after the heaters had been lighted. Later the shaded area will completely fill in the space below the 25 foot level. In this case the thickness of the stratum of air heated is 25 feet and the temperature rise secured at an elevation of 5 feet above the ground is 5° F.

(With acknowledgements to the U.S. Dept. of Agriculture's Farmers' Bulletin, No. 1588.)

concentration of fifty heater pots, each of two or three gallons oil capacity, may be adequate to raise the temperature of the air within the block by the five or six degrees needed to counteract a fairly severe frost (see Plate 2).

In this case, as in the largest scale of static orchard heating (static or stationary as contrasted with the killing of cold-air flows at strategic points before they have begun to produce an accumulation of cold air), the larger the number of heaters to the acre the better, provided that they are of small heat producing capacity. A few large heaters might seem to be much easier to work and look

after but a few columns of very hot air are not desirable since they
have an initial upward impetus which takes them to a much higher
ceiling than the greater number of less heated columns of air from
many heaters. The ideal is to heat only that amount and depth of
air which will prevent frost damage to the fruit trees within it.

The London area offers a fine example of heat inversion, the
distribution of warm air-currents from its innumerable chimneys
having an excellent effect in delaying frost damage in Autumn
and Spring.[1] It is quite common in Spring to find such early
flowering trees as magnolia in full undamaged bloom in London
gardens, while the suburban specimen in a comparable site is
browned by frost. In Autumn, chrysanthemums and dahlias,
though excessively sooty, are often quite undamaged long after
those in low-lying areas have been destroyed.

Large Frosty Areas

In the case of the large sized frost-hole such as one finds in
the Kentish weald, behind the South Downs in West Sussex, and
in the Wye valley around Ross-on-Wye, all areas of more or less
flat, bottom land with much higher land all around, the frost
can be severe and the inversion ceiling may be from fifty to a
hundred feet above soil-level. Such a ceiling must demand a
much greater concentration of heaters to the acre to effect and
maintain inversion against the severe frost temperatures down
below and it is likely that on fifty-acre sections not less than 150
heater pots to the acre, each burning up to three gallons apiece
during the danger period of the night, would be needed to give
protection in a major frost.

Valleys

Here again the deciding factors requiring estimation are the
height and extent of the higher land from which cooled air will
run, the possibility of extremely cold feeds where drainage air is
deep, the extent of the reception area, since valleys vary greatly
in width and length, and the gradation of the valley bottom from
its head to its outlet, if it has an outlet.

If, as a sample, we consider the valley of the Great Stour in

[1] The fruit at the John Innes Horticultural Institution, Merton Park, London,
S.W.19, is a good example of freedom from most frosts. The London atmosphere
also with its sulphurous content makes it impossible for these trees to be infected by
apple or pear scab.

Kent running from Wye to Canterbury, with a fall of some 80 feet in over seven miles and with a bottom at the Canterbury end no more than 60 feet above sea-level, while the valley sides and higher land beyond are from 250 to over 400 feet, we have a large-scale valley frost-hole capable of accepting inundation frosts of considerable depth. There is here every inducement for chilled air to pool and move sluggishly. Near Canterbury are well-grown Bramley orchards set across the valley bottom and on pre-war occasions when these were orchard heated the sluggish air-flow carried the soot from the heaters on to the washing hung out to dry by the residents of Canterbury, resulting in some small local bitterness and recrimination.

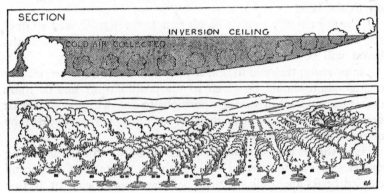

FIG. 11.—Showing how a shelter belt set across a slope may assist in orchard heating by providing depth of cold air for inversion.

This area could be easily heated if heating were on a considerable scale, but the ceiling would tend to be high where only a small acreage was tackled, and for the best results it is likely that over a hundred heaters to the acre would be needed during the most severe spring frosts.

Orchard Heating on Slopes and Hill-sides

This should, of course, not be necessary if proper precautions regarding unimpeded air-flows are taken, but there are times when circumstances make it needful. Though large-scale orchard heating must give the best results on nearly level land one does occasionally see orchards which are on sloping ground with woodland (often belonging to someone else) at the lowest part which has been left, or even planted, to act as a shelter belt and which merely succeeds in backing up cold-air drainage. Where such barriers are of considerable extent they can at times provide a ceiling of cold pooled air up to tree-top level, giving admirable conditions for small-scale orchard heating (see Fig. 11, p. 87).

To judge the possibilities in such cases one should visualise the site in section, noting the fall of the land and the height of the shelter belt, and where a horizontal line projected back from the tree-top level cuts the line of the fall of the land. The area within those lines will be the area to heat and the heater concentration can begin up the slope in quite a small way, attaining its major concentration about the centre or slightly lower down the slope and up to the belt.

The normal fifty to sixty heater pots to the acre divided up over the acreage should be sufficient. The denser the shelter belt the better will be the inversion.

In assessing the need to heat any heatable area on a slope primary consideration should be given to the possibility of one or more heater barrages set in strategic positions to deal with the chilled air draining on to such sites, their flows being always decided by obvious land contours.

One should also consider how far the bottom of the impeding shelter belt can be opened up, whether low branches scrub and tangled briars are really necessary and essential as wind protection and whether the undergrowth cannot be grubbed, the grass and weed beneath the trees kept brushed and the tree-stems themselves pollarded up to six or eight feet thus allowing a fairly free flow of air through the bottom of the belt (Plate 10).

There is always air movement through a belt which is blocking cold-air drainage once cold air has backed up behind it. This is so because the collected cold air having achieved depth has also acquired weight and weight means pressure. Theoretically, if cold air draining down a slope is held up by a barrier fifteen feet high and the cold air behind the barrier stands at a temperature of 26° F. (at which temperature a cubic foot of air weighs ·0820 lbs.) while the general air temperature on the lower side of the barrier stands at 34° F. (air here weighs ·0806 lbs. per cubic foot), then, if a hole three feet in diameter were cut through the base of the barrier, the cold air from behind the barrier would be forced through the hole with a velocity of 4·2 feet per second which, if friction loss be

A promising Bramley orchard rescued by a Kent grower from the jungle below.

Five years before the upper photograph was taken it was in this condition.

20

An expert who insisted on being included, examining Bramley's Seedling apples for "frost eye" in 1943.

In 1944 the same tree carried only one apple frost-eyed and open-cored, shown as the centre fruit in the plate below.

21

Typical sound specimens of Bramley's Seedling and an advanced type of "frost-eye."
Half natural size.

Photo: H. Connold

disregarded, means that a bulk of 108,000 cubic feet of cold air per hour would be passed.

From this it will be realised that while a wall or a hole-free fence will hold up cold air to the exact level of its top (I have personally had fruit killed on the back side of a wall while individual fruits standing two inches above the wall-top level remained undamaged), then a shelter belt receiving large supplies of cold air may also back up cold air to the level of its top while passing an appreciable amount through gaps and holes in its base. How much, if at all, this penetration can reduce the depth of cold air pooling behind the barrier can only be determined by local conditions and contours of which we have already said quite enough.

A good many experiments on heating shallow slopes are needed before any rules can be laid down. Inversion begins soon after the heaters are lit up, but since there is always a downhill air drift on a slope under radiation conditions the inverted air does not perform its normal cycle of rise, inversion and return to source but the warmed air, having risen at a slight angle from the horizontal, will begin to come down again farther down the slope.

It is possible, therefore, to have a considerable block of heaters pushing warmed air heavenwards indefinitely without warming up the air within the area it is desired to heat except for the small amount donated to objects really close to the heaters.

I saw a good example of that in 1938 on a large apple orchard, the Cox's Orange Pippins in one section which I examined closely (even to counting the apples per tree), carrying little or no fruit except where the trees were literally blackened by their nearness to the heater pots and their immersion in smoke. In that particular instance some good came of the lost inversion since market gardeners growing runner beans on land some distance below reported excellent frost protection and harvested good crops.

When operating orchard heating in small valleys it is usual when the heaters are first lit to find the considerable flame from the open type of heater inclined in one direction. This is due to the drift of the local cold-air flow from the nearest higher land. Later, it may be noted that the heater flames have suddenly switched over to an entirely different angle. This is due to the advent of a main flow of cold air which may have travelled some miles from a neighbouring but connecting valley and obliterates the lesser local air-flow.

G

Cold Air invasion from below

Many orchards situated on the lower slopes of hills falling to frosty levels may suffer no damage at all in minor frosts but are liable to gradual invasion by cold air from below in major frosts as the pooling level of collecting cold air rises. I think that it is possible that such invasion owing to its very slow and steady advance may be open to unusual methods of control.

Before the War I was interested in protecting an orchard of this type. Set well up on a good slope and even too well protected by dense shelter hedges it became obvious that, while each heavily hedged section was holding up air drainage from and within its own confines, the lowest section of all, which was closely planted with dwarf pyramid apples, had no outlet to lower levels and during major frosts was actually invaded by the gradual rise of the level of collecting cold air in the valley just below it.

Since at no time did this collection of cold air overtop the orchard level by more than ten feet, its rise to that level must have been very slow and gradual and an unusual method of barrage heating was proposed. The lower end and the last 100 feet of each side of the little orchard were protected by a continuous line of metal radiators. These were on Mr. Buggé's principle (described in Chapter XVII, page 102), of using an intensely hot flame to heat air at one end of a long inverted U sheet-metal tunnel, the air being allowed to run the length of the tunnel which sloped slightly upwards. Thus, in place of a line of heater pots (which might have been equally effective), the equivalent of a hot-water pipe was run round the exposed part of the orchard. In order to steady the air near the heater line, and to reduce invasion of cold air from below to a minimum, a screen of hop-screening, twelve feet high, was erected and this stood between the valley cold air and the heater barrage (see Plate 7).

When the series of heaters, fed with paraffin fuel under pressure from a small motor compressor, was in operation an unbroken line of very warm rising air was maintained at the strategic position to combat invasion. Since the screening itself hindered air movement very considerably it was considered that the rising warm air ought to be able to look after such cold air as came through. Since the heat of the air within the tunnel scorched the grass directly below there was no possibility of cold air entry below. Unfortunately the War prevented any proper trial of this set-up but opportunity to do so may come later.

Hop-screening in Use

Hop-screening might be usefully employed where quite small-scale heating was needed. It would operate in two ways. It would hinder the influx of cold air and if high enough would provide a ceiling for inversion by preventing air movement behind it. If used it would be vital to carry the screening from soil-level upwards and to leave no entry for cold air near soil-level. Any site liable to damage by deep frost would of course be ruled out.

There should be no reason to leave hop-screening used for such protection out of doors for long periods. If permanent poles and wires are erected the screening can be quickly hooked up into place and as easily removed again when the need for it is past. The hop grower, who also grows fruit and is anxious to try out small-scale heating, is in the happy position of already possessing this valuable material and having no particular need for it on his hops at such times as in late April and May when it might prove useful for protecting apple blossom, and for giving much shelter against wind to aid pollinating bees.

CHAPTER XVI

THE MECHANICS OF FROST PREVENTION

PRIOR to the introduction of oil-burning heaters for orchards little could be done by the fruitgrower to save his crops from frost damage. Freedom from frost of any given site was usually regarded as luck, though by some, higher land was known to go with such good fortune.

Smudging or smoking the area to be protected by lighting bonfires in and around the orchard gave rather irregular and unreliable results because of the difficulty of maintaining the smoke where it was needed and because little or no idea of the principles of direct radiation loss, which smoke cover is able to prevent, was understood. Probably those who reported the greatest success from smudging were the growers whose land least needed such protection.

The only good which smoke can do is to reduce radiation loss by interposing a cloud substitute between the earth and a clear sky. Provided that the smoke was thick and well maintained this might reduce radiation loss to such an extent that the ground below the smoke would be as much as 5 or 6 degrees higher than exposed land outside it. We have seen in Chapter XI that an object immersed in air at a temperature not actually low enough to cause damage may lose additional heat by direct radiation loss to that extent. Smoke cover will prevent much direct radiation loss (see Chap. X, p. 51).

Since such diaphanous cover as smoke can be effective in reducing radiation loss some importance can be credited to an artificial fog generator advertised before the war by a Berlin firm.

A system which has no doubt been perfected for war purposes in the past six years.

Artificial Fog.

The inventors claim that the protective blanket of clouds in the night sky, which we all know will prevent or dissipate frost, can be duplicated near soil-level by this artificial fog which they claim will reduce radiation loss by some six degrees.

The apparatus is in two main parts, the whole looking rather like one small drum horizontally poised upon a vertical drum.

The lower drum contains small, lump lime and the other some six gallons of " fog-acid " (sulphurtrioxide in chlorsulphonic acid, for the benefit of those chemically minded). The acid is sprayed upon the lime and a fog is produced and ejected under pressure, one charge lasting for five hours.

This period seems hardly long enough for major frosts, but possibly the makers wish to sell enough fog machines for the grower to run them in duplicate, the recommended concentration being a line of machines at intervals of 100 to 150 feet. The position of such machines would be in lines across the fall of the land or if on level land across the line of prevailing valley bottom drainage. (See Note 3 in Appendix.)

Genuine Fog

There are probably very few growers indeed in a position to create fog on a frosty night from its components, warmth, moisture and cold. An American business man with a citrus and date " ranch " in Arizona told me some years ago that in that dry and arid land where evaporation can be as high as eight times the annual rainfall (our English maximum evaporation is little more than half our total rainfall) irrigation is an absolute necessity. Water from artesian wells is piped to the end of every tree row, this water standing at 70° F. all the year round. When radiation frost threatens all that is necessary is to turn on the irrigation water, and as it flows down the irrigation trenches air temperature rises and the whole orchard is soon blanketed in genuine fog.

Smoke and Heat

In the North of India, in a district where deciduous fruits grow well, it has been reported that good results were experienced in a vineyard by smudging the vines against a radiation frost. The concentration of fires, burning dried dung and litter, was enormous, being 400 to the acre! In practice such a concentration of small sources of heat is ideal, and coupled with the smoke it is little wonder that as much as 10° of added warmth was claimed for the operation. The difficulty of lighting up such a number of fires would be considerable. Although India is beyond our reach a good idea of the heat and smoke provided by a concentration of so many small bonfires can easily be experienced by any third-class railway passenger in a suburban smoking carriage during the rush-hour traffic.

High Smoke Screen Laying

Many years ago when trials of aerial smoke screen laying were in progress I urged the authorities to take temperature readings below the screen on radiation nights. Although, apparently, it has not yet been tried out, there seems reason for supposing that an aeroplane laying and maintaining a smoke screen over a moderate sized and self-contained frost-hole (the Leckford valley described in Chapter VII would be a fair sample) would be able to cut down radiation loss to a considerable extent. If successful on a small-scale frost-hole there is no reason why the system should not be equally useful in large frost-holes using more aeroplanes and more smoke.

Smoke, as generated by war bombs and appliances is, however, of chemical origin and contains no water in suspension, as do genuine clouds and fog, and what proportion of radiated heat would be reflected back from such smoke particles could only be estimated by trial and observation. The effect also of the deposit on crops and property beneath the smoke would have to be considered.

The vapour trails of planes at times grow into surprisingly large clouds (see Plate 5, page 17), but if this is to take place certain definite atmospheric conditions must be present and it is unlikely that vapour trails could be expected to form with any certainty on a radiation frost night save at high altitudes.[1] To be effective against frost clouds must be reasonably low, anything in the nature of cirrus cloud is too thin to offer any substantial check to radiation loss.

During this war extensive use has been made of oil-burning pots designed to create enough smoke to hide vital war-target towns against bombing. A great many of these large-sized heaters should be available after the war at a cheap rate since they have no useful peace-time purpose. Some adaptation on the lines of the improved Harrington heater chimney might adapt them to burn with more heat and less smoke and thus turn a war liability into a peace asset.

Orchard Heaters

The heaters as originally used in American orchards, particularly in the citrus orchards of California, burned fuel oil with considerable

---

[1] Some hold that vapour trails are caused by the exhaust gases from plane engines A more likely explanation and one which will account for the occasionally visible trail from the square-cut end of a Mustang's wings, is that the speed of the propeller's rotation causes a local reduction of temperature. The reduced temperature would cause the air to throw out part of its moisture as vapour.

flame and smoke. Yellow flame, as every schoolboy knows, indicates incomplete combustion, with less heat and more soot than complete combustion would give. In Los Angeles State up to 1st October, 1940, only one gramme of soot per minute was allowed during the burning of each heater. There is, however, no limit to the number of heaters which can be used per acre. After that date only half a gramme of soot per minute was allowed, and the penalty for exceeding this is a fine of up to five hundred dollars or six months in gaol. Residents of Canterbury may appreciate this information and introduce legislation accordingly.

Some idea of the immense reliance which the citrus growers place on orchard heating may be gathered when it is realised that in one night in early January, in 1937, five million heaters, each burning an average of one gallon of oil per hour, operated by sixteen thousand fruitgrowers on an acreage of sixty thousand, burned thirty-two million gallons of oil. Nor was the whole crop saved and much of the fruit had to be passed before X-ray viewing screens to make sure which oranges and grape fruits were sound internally.

The cutting down of soot emission by an approach to the blue flame of complete combustion in America was followed by similar improvements to the English type of heater. By 1939 burner tubes were made available for two- and three-gallon models.

These heater pots before adaptation to chimney burners are circular steel drums capable of holding 2 or 3 gallons of fuel oil. The tops are half covered in, with a lid to complete the cover easily removed when lighting up was necessary. A series of holes a few inches below the top of the drum admit such air as is needed to ensure combustion when the oil has become heated and gives off gas. To start this an asbestos wick dipping into the oil is lit and thereafter the heater functions until such time as the oil is exhausted or the lid is put on to put the flame out. I am told that 100,000 of these heaters have been supplied to English growers.

Fuels

The comparative heat value of the various possible fuels and their relative cost are of importance to fruitgrowers. Under war-time conditions fuel costs are almost prohibitive and the exigencies of the black-out complicates matters, since a grower who obtains permission to light up is at the mercy of the local authorities and may have to dowse his pots at the first bleat of the local siren.

Bitter experience of the past war and of the permanence of a price once risen convinces the author that there is no likelihood of war prices ever dropping near pre-war level. Time was, in the days prior to World War No. 1, when the motorist could buy pure benzole at ninepence a gallon, and even before World War No. 2, petrol was landed in this country at a shade over a penny a gallon though taxation, distribution and wholesale and retail profit raised it to over a shilling. We are therefore very unlikely to see fuel oil back to the 1936 price of fivepence a gallon.

The heat value of oil is 18,000 British Thermal Units per pound of fuel consumed. As a comparison the heat value of a pound of coal is 13,000 B.T.U. When price is compared, good coal at £2 a ton (it really could be bought for that in 1936), the unit cost of oil against coal was 1 to 0·55 in favour of coal. They are unlikely to vary much in ratio after the war, though coal rose by 3s. 6d. a ton in the summer of 1945.

The advantages of coke-heaters against coal or oil were suggested and patents were applied for in 1935. A specimen of one of these heaters was shown at the East Malling Frost Conference, in 1938. These were calculated to be more economical than oil or coal, and at sixty to the acre they were expected to provide better heating. The following tables give comparative costs of installation and maintenance in 1936.

ORCHARD HEATING USING OIL-BURNING HEATERS
Table No 1. Initial Outlay (*One Acre*).

	£	s.	d.
60 Heaters at say 3s. 2d	9	10	0
60 Asbestos Wicks at 2d.	0	10	0
Frost Predictor	1	17	6
Alarm Thermometer	1	15	0
Electric Bell and Sundries	1	7	6
	£15	0	0

Annual cost per acre assuming depreciation over 4 years, £3 15s.

Table No 2. Average cost of oil for one night (*One Acre*)

Each heater consumes approximately 1 gallon of fuel oil in 3½ hours: it is very unusual for a frost to persist more than 4½ hours on any one occasion and sometimes it is less. The number of frosts experienced in one season over the last fifteen years (i.e. 1921 to 1936) has never exceeded 4, and *the average is 2 frosts per season.**

* This estimate can be compared with the temperature recorded on the two graphs on page 33, both of which relate to frosty orchard sites and hardly confirm the estimate,

Each "light up" of say 4½ hours therefore costs (assuming the averag cost of fuel oil is 5*d*.) 60 × 1¼ gallons at 5*d*. per gallon approximately £1 11*s*. 6*d*.

Cost of protection for one year with one killing frost (initial outlay £3 15*s*. ; fuel oil, £1 11*s*. 6*d*.) £5 6*s*. 6*d*.

Table No 3. Annual total cost per acre with 0–4 "light ups" on various acreages.

Annual cost per acre for protection based on Tables 1 and 2.

	No Frost. Equipment only.	1 Frost.	2 Frosts.	3 Frosts.	4 Frosts.
	£ *s.* *d.*	£ *s.* *d.*	£ *s.* *d.*	£ *s.* *d.*	£ *s.* *d.*
1 acre . . .	3 15 0	5 6 6	6 18 0	8 9 6	10 1 0
5 acres . . .	2 15 0	4 6 6	5 18 0	7 9 6	9 1 0
10 acres . . .	2 12 6	4 4 0	5 15 6	7 7 0	8 18 6
25 acres . . .	2 11 0	4 2 6	5 14 0	7 5 6	8 17 0

Variation in cost per acre. This reaches its maximum on one acre due to the fact that one frost predictor, alarm thermometer, etc., would be sufficient irrespective of the number of heaters used, provided the acreage is all in one block.

NOTE.—*Cost of labour and storage accommodation* are dependent on the size of installation and vary according to individual conditions. For this reason, these two items are not included in the above figures.

(Geo Monro, Ltd., *Protection of Crops against Frost*, 1936.)

Coke-burning heaters. Operating costs of orchard heating.

Initial Outlay per Acre

	£	*s.*	*d.*
60 Heaters at 10*s*.	30	0	0
Frost Predictor	1	17	6
Alarm Thermometer	1	15	0
Electric Bell and Sundries	1	7	6
Storage Bin for Coke and Gear . . .	1	10	0
Reserve of Coke at 40*s*. a ton . . .	5	0	0
	£41	10	0

Depreciation

	£	*s.*	*d.*
20% on £30 (heaters lasting five years) . .	6	0	0
20% on £5 0 0	1	0	0
10% on £3 10 0	0	7	0
Interest : 5% on £41 10 0	2	1	6
	£9	8	6

Average annual cost per acre :

Presuming 3 " light-ups " per season for frosts of 6 hours' duration.

	£	s.	d.
Coke at 40s. per ton	4	16	6
Annual Depreciation and Interest	9	8	6
Kindling	0	6	0
Labour (about)	1	0	0
	£15	11	0

Compare cost of oil heating ; 60 heaters per acre at 4s. 6d. each, lasting 5 years, using oil at 5½d. per gallon, and making necessary provision for oil storage, reserve of fuel, etc., calculated on same basis as above, £17 to £18.

(*From Coke for Orchard Heating*, issued by The London and Counties Coke Association, London, S.W.1.)

These figures are taken direct from the handbooks published by the makers and reprinted with acknowledgments but no comments.

No attempt appears to have been made to use gas heating. In orchards well served by underground spray mains, draw-off mains fitted with series of burners could easily be laid out and lit. Such an installation would mean the employment of a small gas-holder but this should be little more expensive than the large permanent storage tank needed for holding fuel oil and if the gasometer was partially emptied by a night's heating refilling from the main would be a much simpler and cleaner job than would oil re-fuelling. The only proviso would be the presence of a gas main near enough to the orchard and many of my fruitgrower friends have neither gas nor electricity.

Electric Heating

Pictures have appeared in American science magazines of citrus orchards strung with overhead power lines carrying radiant heat diffusers on the lines of the bowl fires which can be run off any electric-lamp-plug. Provided one had cheap current this would be a perfectly sound idea, but cheap power is very hard to come by in England. Were it obtainable its chief horticultural use would be the large-scale heating of market garden soil for out of season crops.

CHAPTER XVII

KILLING COLD-AIR FLOWS

SINCE the heating of orchards pre-supposes the collection of a big depth of cold air, it is curious that no attempts have been recorded to prevent that collection. Obviously, no attempt could be usefully made to do this in one of the large frosty areas, but there are many individual orchards which are frosted in part, or in whole, as the result of quite local air-drainage which must flow down certain definite channels which the land contours determine.

The pictures on Plate 6A, illustrate parts of the frost collecting areas and the channel down which cold air from over seven hundred acres of grass land drain down to a natural barrier of trees set across a narrow valley. Drainage backs up there and, having reached the tops of the trees, falls to the orchard beneath and continues its course through more than half a mile of full-grown apple trees to the bottom of the valley. Its exit from the valley was, at the time the photos were taken, badly impeded by a high shelter belt planted by a neighbour to shut off the orchard above.

The owner of the orchard is a very wide-awake man, anxious to do the best for his fruit, and we decided to try out some experiments together. Across his valley above the fruit at the spot where the natural barrier of trees stood he erected a high screen of hessian supported by wires (Plate 6B). The idea of this erection was to see how far we could collect and back up cold air to a definite level at this spot, for in dealing with an enemy in a case like this it is helpful to have his measure.

On an estimated possible build-up of ten feet of depth of frosty air during a radiation night [1] air drainage to pass this amount from the land above the screen was 65,729,500 cubic feet. This sounds a formidable figure " *en masse*," but spread it out into cubic feet of flow per minute through the valley and in an eight-hour night it is no great amount. Probably at the height of the frost it would not exceed 250,000 cubic feet a minute.

---

[1] This figure was purposely taken to be on the safe side. The ten-foot build-up on flat land is known to have taken place in the 1935 and 1938 frosts, but that was on the level and in stagnant air conditions. It is probable that no more than half this amount per square foot of drainage area would have flowed down the valley, since the temperature of the moving air would have been several degrees higher than stagnant air with a much slower build-up as a result.

Now cold air draining off high land devoid of gullies is unlikely to be at a temperature much lower than 30° F., whereas air which has pooled and is being rapidly chilled down by intense radiation loss from the objects immersed in it may easily stand at 22° F. You may, therefore, have a difference of eight degrees between the feed air and the lower layers of collected air. Surely then to raise the temperature of the air flowing down to fill the frost-hole should be a much easier proposition than heating the whole mass of extremely cold air after it has collected? Moreover, if one can raise the temperature of that draining air by a mere three or four degrees it will be as warm as the air above it and will then have no incentive to travel having lost the density which set it in motion. In fact the cold-air feed will have been killed.

To many sensible people who have not studied frost this idea of killing cold-air feeds may sound pure nonsense but, given the ideal conditions, it is an easy and obvious proposition.

In the days just before the war my friend and I had ideas of a permanent barrage across the upper valley with concrete well-sections set in the base of the dam through which the collecting cold air would be sucked by electric fans, warmed by heater units and ejected on the lower side robbed of all its frosty potentialities. The amount of cold air to be tackled was no more than is handled by any large hotel's air conditioning plant, so the cost was not out of proportion for the benefits conferred.

Such a system would have manifold advantages and con-veniencies. It could be operated with no labour or supervision. It would start up and stop under thermostatic control. Considering that the orchard below was needing some thousands of heater pots and had to be warmed up several times in any cold Spring the cost of the erection and installation was not felt to be excessive.

The imminence of war prevented the building of this dam but, still anxious to try out the effect of warming up his air flow, the grower first put out a barrage of orchard heater pots, set close together in a double row some 200 yards above the screen, which he lighted up when the air at 4 feet soil-level reached 32° F.

On 11 May, 1939, he wrote:

Of all the frosts we have had this Spring (it has not been a really frosty year), the screen and the barrage have quite definitely dealt with all the cold air that drains into our valley bottom from the very large acreage of land above the screen. I now feel entirely satisfied that the theory of cold-air drainage is absolutely and entirely correct and that the possibilities of damming up cold air and killing it at source are enormous. I should estimate the cost of dealing with it in this way, as opposed to orchard heaters after it has arrived, to be somewhere between one-third and one-quarter.

In the frost of 1944, however, this grower has seen fit to change his opinion, having suffered severe and general frost damage throughout his plantations, whether on the higher land, which is inclined to be level, or on the slopes and sides of his frosty-bottomed valley. This without lighting up his orchard heater equipment.

A change of opinion is a sign of a receptive and elastic mind and the fruitgrower is continually having to change his views and accept new explanations regarding his problems. In frost damage we are dealing with one factor only—the Law of Gravity—and a true explanation of the cause of unusual or unexpected behaviour of cold air must be forthcoming if one knows where to look for it.

It would seem that the 1940 frost set-up began with a persistent drift of cold, heavy anticyclonic air which swept inland from below the Wisbech area in a curve embracing the Eastern, South-eastern and Southern counties almost to the Isle of Wight. The West Midlands were not included in the low temperature drift since little serious frost damage occurred on many sites known to be liable in major Spring frosts. Devon and the South-west also escaped save in a few badly sited areas.

The particular farm in question, where the killing of cold-air flows in 1939 gave great promise, is in the North-east Essex area and with no higher land between it and the sea. It embraces orchard land which, though well up, is inclined to be level in parts, while the valley and valley sides which bisect the flat areas are also planted to fruit. If we assume that the anticyclonic air-drift met the drainage air from this fruit farm with a persistent counter pressure of quite cold air moving forward at a few miles an hour it is reasonable to suppose that this would prevent the normal air drainage from his site being fully effective and the resultant radiation loss due to stagnant air would cause damage to much of his blossom or fruitlets.

It is usually assumed that a radiation frost demands a condition of calm air, but if complete immobility of air is meant by that then the condition is non-existent as soon as large-scale air drainage begins to operate. One must also allow for the forward movement of the mass of cold anticyclonic air which provides the necessary conditions for the spring frost to begin.

In many sites visited in frosty years I have in no single instance found serious frost damage where planting was on high ground *with a good fall* and with ample space between the trees to allow for air-drainage.

My friend concludes his letter by adding : " One can in this job be so definite in one's opinion in one year and hold the opposite opinion in the next that instead of being classed as a thinker one is apt to be regarded as a liar."

I quite agree and so we had better let the problem of killing cold-air flows be decided at a later date, postulating it as a theory which may not be workable in all cases but certainly should be in some.

The " Tunnel " Heater

It is common knowledge that cold air moving in warmer air will cling tenaciously to the lowest level available. Heated air is equally insistent on staying up and this was taken advantage of by Mr. Buggé, of Sittingbourne, in Kent, to produce a " tunnel " heater.

To form the tunnel he takes iron sheets six feet square and bends each into an inverted U shape, splaying the bottom slightly outward and aiming at a flat top rather than a round one. Six or more sections are then put end to end with the open bottom facing the ground in a continuous line. The first section rests on the ground and the following sections are supported and gradually raised so that at the end of a thirty-four foot tunnel there is a rise of a foot. This rise of one foot in thirty-four was found to be enough to maintain the flow of heated air at the top of the tunnel.

Beneath the first section and aimed along the tunnel is fixed an atomising burner of the type used for brazing, supplied with pressure-fed paraffin from a small motor compressor capable of feeding six burners via a pipe-line. The burner is the expensive item in this heater, costing pre-war about seven guineas. It functions at 18 to 20 lbs. pressure, taking one and three-quarters of a gallon of oil per hour, each gallon providing 190,500 B.T.U. of heat.

On the day when I saw several of these tunnel heaters set out in a disused chalk quarry it was blowing a south-westerly gale and raining. The chalk pit, about thirty feet deep and two hundred yards long, was full of gusty winds, but the heated air was still travelling well along the several tunnels which were in operation. I took a temperature reading of the air at the tunnel end and found it to fluctuate between 166° F. and 220° F. Mr. Buggé told me that under windless conditions using a fifty-four foot run of tunnel, he had registered 200° C.

Very little of this form of heating has been tried. Initial expense is heavy, for a compressor costs over £50, and it is obviously unsuited for general orchard heating since the maximum of small sources of heat are preferable to a few large sources of heat for obtaining inversion.

In practice one has available a rising barrage of heat from the whole length of the tunnel. The metal becomes extremely hot and a great deal of heat is radiated downwards on to the ground. A few of these barrage heaters might form a useful line to tackle a cold-air current flowing down a slope or to look after invasion from below as a valley becomes submerged in pooling cold air. This latter aspect is dealt with on page 90, and illustrations of the tunnel are also given on Plate 7, page 25.

Anti-freeze Spraying

A few years ago two Americans patented an anti-freeze spray for fruit trees. Their claims were so surprising that the matter may be worth reporting in full. The composition of the wash was as follows :

Stock Solution A.
    1 gallon of kerosene.
    16 ounces of sulphonated mineral oil or sulphonated bitumen,
        or 4 ounces ammonium caseinate,
        or 8 ounces potassium caseinate,
        or 4 ounces laundry soap.
    All heated to boiling-point.

Stock Solution B.
    4 ounces glycerine or honey.
    1 ounce powdered blood,
        or albumin spreader.
    2 gallons of water.
    Bring to boiling-point.

    Mix A and B, and while mixing add 10 ounces of alcohol (denatured or wood).

At a concentration of 30 of water to 1 of stock solution protection against freezing is given down to 30° F.

25 parts water	25° F.
20 parts water	20° F.
15 parts water	15° F.
10 parts water	10° F.

Trials with glycerine solution in this country suggest that enough can be absorbed to raise the resistance of plant tissues to frost, but, even if protection could be assured, few growers could afford the expense or get round their orchards in time to prevent damage. Americans usually get quite long notice of an approaching freeze since their catastrophes travel thousands of miles down to the citrus-growing areas and are quite a different proposition to our homely little freezes.

At the same time, if the wash were applied at the late pink-bud stage the formula containing honey might prove attractive to pollinating bees when the blossom came out.

I distrust the powdered blood addition, since this might well turn them from nectar-sipping habits to vampirish ways with dire results to the beekeeper. Fortunately the addition of nitrates does not enter into the formula, as had this been the case nitro-glycerine might have gone to the bees heads and literally have resulted in " buzz-bombs " by the hundred thousand. So, perhaps, we had better leave the anti-freeze inventors to preach their gospel to their own brave new world until such time as complete results are forthcoming. (See Note 4 in Appendix.)

" Brush " Protecting

The American horticulturists recognise the value of protecting against direct radiation loss and in the Imperial Valley, California, a rather elaborate method (Fig. 12) has been evolved for protecting and stimulating tender plants which was reported in the American Meteorological Magazine. Although this hardly affects the fruit-grower it might be possible to raise earlier strawberries by the same system or some adaptation of it.

The ground is ridged from East to West into continuous mounds five feet apart and eighteen inches high. Stakes are driven in at the ends of the rows and at intervals down the rows in order to support two strained wires. Then protective, waterproofed paper is laid along the wires and secured by straight canes of " arrow-weed," with the feathered tips left in place. Presumably the canes are pushed into the bed on alternate sides of the paper which would be in the form of a continuous roll (probably the mulching paper which was obtainable before the war in England for putting between rows of plants or for sowing seeds through to get a weedless row). The paper will, therefore, tilt from North to South and run from East to West, while the soil below it will receive full sun heat plus

Restricted air-drainage through over-close planting and deep grass.

Good, wide planting, but air flow blocked by nuts planted beneath the trees.

22

Photos: Shell Film Unit

GREEN-CLUSTER STAGE
It seems possible that "Cracked-russet" damage can begin about this stage, i.e., in early to mid-April.

PINK-BUD STAGE
Definitely susceptible to frost, but much more resistant than full bloom. Mid-April to late.

PETAL-FALL STAGE
Very susceptible to frost and still to suffer the "June drop." Late April to early May.

23

Critical apple leaf damage—photographed in early June, one month after damage. Fruitlets have all fallen off by severe frosts of May 7-10, 1944

at the base of the tower, a big bonfire sent warmed air upwards for the propeller to spread down among the orchard trees below.

All these machines depend upon their ability to force warm air to take the place of cold or to mechanically mix both to produce a non-damaging temperature. This may sound a fairly simple matter, but in practice it is extremely difficult. The warmer the air at the tower-top level (whether it be heated or not) in comparison with the air near ground-level, the more difficult it must be to persuade it to go down since its natural habit is to rise and cold air is forever forcing it upwards in order to secure the lowest place.

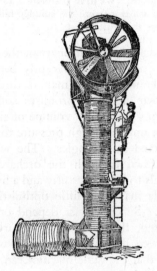

Fig. 13.—" Frost-Blower."   (After a photo in Popular Science, U.S.A.)

Whatever heating is done should take place at or as near as possible to soil-level for the rise of any warmed air is inevitable.

The following letter from a Californian citrus grower, written in October 1938, gives the general feeling of the intelligent orchardist regarding such machines, despite the fact that at that time some 150 were in use in California representing a capital outlay of nearly half a million dollars.

We are abandoning the frost machine because in all our tests with the machine, under every climatic condition, it has proved inefficient and un-successful. In the big freeze of 1937 our entire crop froze with the frost machine in operation day and night ; whereas some growers saved a portion of their crop by smudging. But in a good many cases of fruit saved that year by smudging, the oil or coal bill was greater than the returns brought by the fruit saved.

To the point then ; I certainly would not advise anyone to invest in or waste time with any sort of frost extinguisher system.   The principle under which the frost machine is supposed to work, that of creating a ceiling or manufacturing wind currents, etc., in order to prevent the temperature from reaching the freezing-point is O.K., but it would take a motor of such tremendous horse-power to make the principle effective that your farmer simply could not afford to install it or foot the bill to operate it.   The frost machine used by us and on acreages all over the State has proved unsuccessful.

If anyone desires frost protection I would advise the application of plenty of heat by oil, or coal-burning smudge pots.   Smudging [1] has proved successful under all climatic conditions.   We have abandoned, for the present, smudging, because in the event of a major freeze the smudge bill would be greater than the returns received for the fruit saved.

A mobile approach to the stationary method of cold air killing, described on page 100, has very recently been made in America by a firm who are famous for the manufacture of spraying pumps. This, from their own account, promises some hope of success. Briefly, the plan is to suck a large volume of air into a wind tunnel and blast it out of a nozzle at high pressure through a flame which is fed by jets directed at all angles.   The whole outfit is trailer mounted and is drawn through the orchard when the frost is developing.   Models to look after fifty and a hundred acre orchards are proposed.   This may be a little optimistic, but smaller areas might well benefit.   Success must depend on the volume of air which can be heated, the amount of disturbance caused by its ejection and the speed with which the orchard can be traversed. A big advantage is that the same machine can, with little modification, be used for the modern type of combined dust and water spraying.

Since the second edition of this book was published several trial mobile machines employing high-power propellers for air disturbance have been made in England.   Some will be tried out in the Spring of 1947.   These machines are all tractor drawn, some of them utilising the power take-off of the tractor.   Others are tractor drawn but self-contained as regards the power unit which varies from a few horse-power to a plane engine delivering one hundred and seventy-five horse-power.

[1] The writer of the letter prefers the word " smudging " to " orchard heating." Since the permitted soot allowance is now so small the latter is the better description.

CHAPTER XIX

ON BECOMING FROST-MINDED

IF the reader of this book accepts the principles of gravitational air flows and collection and development of ultra-cold air in frost-holes he will by now have realised that the time to study a frost is after it has taken place, while the marks of its damage are still obvious and indicative of its travel and collection. Only to those desirous of collating masses of figures are thermometers at all necessary; indeed, unless thermometers are used with a full appreciation of land contours they are positively misleading.

It is, I believe, a fact that anyone who rides a hobby to death becomes a crank. Although a great admirer of the beautiful in colour and scenery I find myself regarding some magnificent panorama such as the Wye Valley at Symond's Yat and thinking, "How perfectly lovely but what a shocking frost-hole there must be up stream if this opening is to take all the frosty air from around Ross."

Probably these are the sentiments of a crank, but they do not mean that in sensing the result of land contours while appreciating a view I have lost all sense of its beauty. Far from it. It is, however, an indication that a habit once formed may persist in obtruding itself.

To the average fruitgrower it is enough if he knows and appreciates the frost risks or frost freedom of his own particular site. He is there for the duration and until he leaves his farm or buys another he is not unduly concerned with other people's troubles. To the would-be fruit planter, especially in the case of the man who proposes to retire and invest his life savings in the hazardous profession of fruit-growing, to be frost-conscious should be a useful asset. For anyone who is likely to be asked to vet land for fruit farm sites (and this applies particularly to horticultural advisers) to be frost minded is an absolute necessity, if his advice is to be worth having.

The habit is easily developed, but it should be begun after a major frost in April or May. Come with me for a personally conducted lesson. We will start from the village of Lingfield by bus and go as far as Caterham, which is a convenient station for London. You can, if you wish, follow us on a large-scale map,

preferably one with the various contours marked in different colours
of the type which Messrs. Bartholomew supply to motorists.

Though I have been a resident of Lingfield since 1936 I cannot
describe it as a nice village save that, like the curate's egg, it is
excellent in parts. In its centre is a pond in the last stages of putrid
decomposition, which is a disgrace to the local council and even
in a fire blitz would be quite useless owing to the dense coating of
litter and rubbish of all kinds which protrude from a thick scum
of green weed. This, you will say, has little to do with frost and
I agree. The pond, however, is on the highest part of Lingfield
and except in one direction the land falls away gently to the North,
South and East. Lingfield is therefore not a frost-hole, and,
though less high than the nearby town of East Grinstead, is itself
a donor area in all save the very worst frosts, when it may come
into the intermediate category.

As the bus leaves the village and reaches open fields the land
to the right slopes away gently to Crowhurst and towards the base
of the hills where lie Oxted and Limpsfield, so that we are now
in a definite intermediate area. We will assume it is the morning
of 11 May, 1944, and that the frosts which began on the 7th have
left their dark stain of frosted foliage on the oaks which are plentiful
in this part of the country. Elms, of course, show no damage
from radiation frost in Spring though they are among the first
trees to react to frost in Autumn.

Long before Blindley Heath is reached we are in a shallow
frosty flat in which the oaks are black from top to bottom indicating
a frost-hole (see Plate 18). Leaving Blindley Heath we rise a
little and at once oak damage becomes patchy indicating an intermediate area, but as we progress over the series of small ups and
downs on the straight stretch towards South Godstone we come
into a very frosty patch indeed. Here the railway embankment
holds up air flows in all manner of places which, by the way, is
characteristic of most embankments (see Fig. 7, p. 42) on more or
less level land. Directly we have passed under the bridge we rise
sharply through the village and are back into a section where oaks
have green leaves again though it is noticeable that enough cold air
has built up in the coppice on top of the rise to blacken the tender
shoots of the young ash saplings.

From here to Godstone proper the country is broken. The
road tends to lie much higher than the country on the right but
has higher land all along to the left side. Just before we reach

the sandpit on the left is a cottage, which, despite the much higher land behind it, stands on a gentle eminence of its own with a good three-way fall. There should be fruit on the trees in its small orchard (a fine crop of apples matured). The row of houses on the right too should have escaped major damage for the land falls well away behind them and there is ample room for collecting cold air. (A good crop of apples was obvious here in early August.)

We pass through one cold pocket on the left just before entering Godstone but beyond, as we begin the rise to Caterham, we seem to be in a different climate (see Plate 18 for typical contrasts). In the far distance to the right one can see a few ash trees black and leafless in the bottom land but here the oaks stand green and happy.

As we drop down the long descent into Caterham high land sloping steeply borders the road on both sides. We have passed the top of the air shed with its donor areas on both sides of the hill and the valley floor along which the bus now runs is a true intermediate area with feeds from both sides. At the last bus-stop by the junction of the main with the by-pass road a frosty bottom on the left is bisected by a road with pretty little houses and gardens on each side of it. Lucky the owner at the top of the U-shaped dip, for he will have fruit where his near neighbour will have none, for along the bottom of the U must pass all the air drainage from the hill-sides behind.

One could, of course, go on describing journeys on these lines indefinitely, but this will be indication enough of how to combine appreciation of nature's charms with a realisation of the behaviour of cold air as dictated by land contours. It should only be complementary to the pleasure taken in observing the countryside.

CHAPTER XX

FROST CONTROL FOR THE GARDEN

THE amateur, having inadvertently purchased this book and waded through its many confusing pages, may feel that whatever the commercial grower may do against frost there is precious little hope for himself. Actually the amateur who lives in a frosty spot can make many interesting trials and experiments on a small scale.

We have already seen (page 56) that the glass cloche confers considerable protection to ground crops such as strawberries, lettuces, etc., and the use of cloches on early crops is growing amazingly to judge by the space in the papers devoted to advertising them. Cloches to many people are expensive luxuries and since the shutting out of the night sky is the main need in frost protection anything which does this is affective. Old asbestos roofing tiles, which can easily be joined with a wire at the top, can be adapted for use as night covering and can serve a useful purpose though less effective than glass. Light lath frames covered with any material from muslin to discarded black-out blinds will also serve. The glass cloche operates in two ways as it conserves sun heat and reflects back heat lost by the plant at night.

Even if asbestos tiles are not available any cover placed over the strawberry rows at night must give a good deal of protection. At times, when the stars were bright,[1] I have gone out with an armful of old newspapers and covered a sizeable patch. The pre-war *Times*, owing to its thick paper, was excellent for this purpose. It is, however, rather a long job and there is often a breeze in the early morning which distributes the sheets all over the garden while rain may come along and turn them into a sodden pulp which must be dried in the sun heat before they can be collected for use again.

I think that a cheap form of roller blind using hessian [2] in

[1] This is really too late to begin covering-up, and one should do the job while the soil is still warm before sunset, when the calm and clearness suggest frost, rather than wait for the temperature drop. But this is a case where " Better late than never " still holds good.

[2] American trials in 1928, using burlap (a material similar to hessian), showed an actual gain in temperature, beneath the cover, of 5·30° F. as compared with the outside of the cover. In this case second-hand sacks were split and sewn together to make a

strips six feet or so wide, which could be fixed at one side of the strawberry bed and unrolled to the opposite side would give excellent protection and could be used again in the autumn for the protection of such plants as tomatoes, dahlias and chrysanthemums. Since blossoms in close contact with exposed hessian will lose heat by that contact it is better to support any covering material above the blossom rather than to let it rest directly upon the plant. A blind of this type hanging against a wall of flowering plums or peaches is extremely useful, while many a fig tree has never given a decent crop of figs until it got winter protection in the shape of a thatched hurdle.

A wall in itself cuts down radiation loss (see p. 55) from trees planted against it, and any temporary or permanent addition in the way of an out-jutting roof from the wall-top reduces the radiation loss still further. On cordon apples and pears the roller blind idea could easily be adopted, since the compactness of the training lends itself to easy covering.

On early potatoes gardeners have found that thin wood boards supported on bricks or flower-pots directly above the tender shoots will give really useful protection in quite severe Spring frosts.

On small individual fruit trees, pears, bush apples, peaches grown as bush trees, and small half-standard plums the ideal protection would be a covering of hessian or other material which could be pushed up on top of a pole so that the cover draped itself in folds around the tree rather like a deflated parachute. Wide long lengths of hessian can be slung over a wire stretched well above the trees so that the covering can be drawn over and tied. This is easy in the case of a row of closely spur-pruned trees. If on a really severe night of Spring frost a candle, or better still a small oil lamp, or best of all a lamp of the type hung within the bonnet of the car, were inserted near the centre of the tree and beneath the covering then local heat inversion would be set up which would be really well maintained and quite effective.

This form of protection would cost money, but I once knew a keen gardener who annually lost his crop of Worcester Pearmains from his single tree through birds and wasps. Determined to keep the varmints away he enclosed the tree in a strong wood

length equal to 185 feet long and 3 feet wide. The strips were rolled from the wheeled axle of a buggy and covered two rows each. These results were also confirmed in 1944, at Cheshunt, in the Lea Valley, where a rise of 6° F. as compared with outside temperature was noted inside muslin cages.

frame over which was stretched fine-meshed metal gauze. It must have cost him over a ten-pound note to put up. He could certainly have bought all the Worcesters he needed for his rapidly declining years for half the money but he won his point. Suppose that you had a bush peach tree capable of carrying 300 peaches, each worth 2s. or £30 the lot, would you grudge an outlay of say thirty shillings to safeguard such a tree from the loss of so valuable a crop?

Rich men as well as poor men find themselves gardening on frosty sites but while the latter may have to grin and bear it the former can do something about it.

The same practice of covering up can be applied to the gooseberry bush or the red or black currant, but here a discarded sack or manure bag will serve, indeed from the last named some essence of fertility may be donated as well as frost protection. Raspberry rows can be covered with a long strip of hessian supported by a strained wire, but there is little need to protect any but the Lloyd George or other early flowerers. Norfolk Giant is late enough to miss any but very late May frosts.

For small, tender plants a brick with a slate atop will be helpful, and such cover can be left in place till the weather changes. Chrysanthemum plants can be profitably grown on frost-free sites, but on low land where an untimely frost in October may spoil the blooms and turn an asset into a liability the plants should be dug up and moved under cover while in bud. It is enough to place them close against a wall with Dutch lights leaning over them if you have no cold greenhouse in which to finish them.

A glass house will give several weeks of additional life to such plants, but even the glass house can be protected by covering over the glass at night, preferably from the inside with blinds. This only applies to clear starry nights when radiation is active.

Do not expect that a bonfire or two in one or more corners of the garden will keep frost away, for it will not. Do not yearn for orchard heating; if you had it you would wake up to blackened sheets, a sooty face and smuts all over the breakfast table.

Plan your garden with discretion and you may get some amelioration of frost severity by planting suceptible subjects in the shelter of dwarf types of evergreens or plants which have good solid foliage and yet are not easily damaged by frost. Use also the shade, or nearness, of trees and hedges which are not at the lowest end of the garden. You can avoid planting the lower spots to such plants as react strongly to frost. The sprouting broccoli will be perfectly happy where the runner bean will perish.

The walled garden, unless it be in a very low spot, will usually ensure crops of fruit on trees planted against the walls themselves, but in the case of walled gardens enclosing an acreage of land, any tilt to one direction will cause a pooling of cold and damaging air on a frosty night at the lowest section of the garden. Then though wall fruit may not suffer, such fruits as gooseberries and currants, or apples and pears growing away from the wall in the open, may be damaged. I know of two such gardens, well enough sited but completely enclosed, and the remedy advised is to set a good, wide gateway in the lowest spot in place of the solid wall, or to bring down the level of the wall to a few feet in height, and set iron rails along the top to keep the level of protection against thieves high enough.

Sometimes a good look round with a surveyor's eye will suggest that a hedge lowered in one place or replaced with an iron hurdle would offer escape for cold air and prevent the build-up of icy air to the level of your hedgetops. Perhaps the elimination of an unwanted shelter belt or even the dense undergrowth at its base would be helpful. Explore the possibilities and remember that you are dealing with a very fluid phenomenon which is just as anxious to escape as you are to be rid of it, and will do so if there is a lower spot to go to.

APPENDIX

NOTE 1: There is no doubt that persistent cold, dry winds when the leaf is young can cause scorched leaf tips owing to the water loss of the leaf by evaporation occurring at a temperature which is too low for the replacement of water by the tree itself. The same wind can affect unopened bud and open blossom.

NOTE 2: A very unusual reaction to frost has been noticeable during recent frosty Springs in the case of the pear Beurré Bedford. After the frost of May 1st, 1945, the damaged fruitlets threw out growths at the side which developed miniature leaves and long stalked blossoms (see Fig. 14). Many of these secondary blossoms set and developed curiously shaped fruits. I showed some to a plant genetecist, who said that he was unable to relate them to frost damage, but the fact that these curiosities have been repeated only after severe Spring frosts seems to me conclusive evidence that frost is the cause of it. A very small proportion of the secondary blooms developed fruits reaching half size and shaped like a normal pear. The remainder were grotesque. All had very long, slender, jointed stalks.

NOTE 3: This method is said to have been used by the Germans for screening their Belgian coastal batteries in 1917–18. A naval commander tells me that chlorosulphonic acid (CS for short) has been standard practice for smoke screens in the Navy since that war. It was applied by squirting the acid on to the hot funnels of destroyers or on to the exhaust pipes of fast motor craft. This to the great annoyance of the engineers, who objected to its intensely corrosive action. Later, trials showed that the acid sprayed into the air under pressure developed fog without the need for heat owing to the natural moisture content of air at sea-level. This would not, however, seem to be a suitable spray for orchards.

NOTE 4: *Blossom Delay by Spraying.* As every fruitgrower knows, the use of petroleum oil sprays for capsid egg control in late February or early March tends to delay the opening of the blossom bud by sealing it over. Where spraying has been begun and re-started owing to weather reasons, or in cases where wind drift during spraying has been heavy, a thicker coating of oil may build up. At times this has caused definite damage, but always it has had some delaying effect on blossom opening.

With the rapid progress now being made in sprays for fruit-setting and to prevent early fruit-fall it seems likely that sprays may be developed capable of delaying blossom by as much as ten days. Then by planting such late-flowering, quality apples as Mr. Tydeman, of East Malling Research Station, is now developing, it should be possible to plant up a frost hole with good sorts of apple which, with the retarding spray application, would not bloom till late in May when serious frost risks are past. These may be visions of the future, but we are on the way to realisation.

FIG. 14.—Fruit cluster of Beurré Bedford.
May 20, 1945.

NOTE 5. A few days before the publication of this book, Technical Communication No. 15, "Spring Frost Damage in Orchards and its possible Prevention," was issued by the I.A.B., Central Sales Branch, Penglais, Aberystwyth, price 1s. 6d. This summarises the various official lines of frost research at home and abroad, and gives a large bibliography to those who are in search of the utmost available detail on the various methods of frost control.

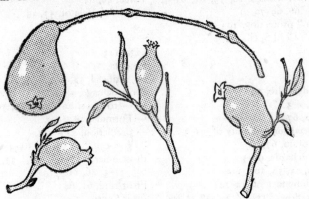

FIG. 15.—Fruits of Beurré Bedford which developed.
September 12, 1945.

INDEX

Vapour trails, 94
Victoria plum, 46, 67, 71

Walled garden, 115
Wall-fruit, 53, 55, 62, 72, 115
Warwickshire Drooper, 67, 71-2
Water, influence of, 26-7, 36
William pear, 70-1

Wind, 14, 46, 50, 62
—, machines for making, 106 *et seq.*
Wisley, 51, 69
Worcester Pearmain, 1 *n.*, 59, 68, 69-70, 115-16
Worcestershire, 74

Yellow Egg plum, 67, 71-2